My Spelling Workbook

My Spelling Workbook – Book F

Offices in: United Kingdom: PO Box 2840, Coventry, CV6 5ZY
Australia: PO Box 332, Greenwood, Western Australia 6924
Republic of Ireland: Bosheen, New Ross, Co. Wexford, Ireland

First Published in 1990, R.I.C. Publications
Revised and Reprinted 2001, Prim -Ed Publishing
ISBN 1 86400 638 2

Introduction

Welcome to *My Spelling Workbook*. This book has lots of different activities to help you improve your spelling. Here are some tips to show you the best way to use your book.

- **Learning Words**

  Each list of words in the book has five test columns. Every time you spell a word correctly in a test, you can tick the column.

  Three ticks in a row show that you know how to spell the word.

  If you do not get three ticks in a row, you write 'T' in the transfer box. When you start your next list of words, you add the word to the table 'Difficult Words I Have Found'. You can also add any other difficult words you find.

- **Look, Say, Cover, Write, Check**

  These words are to remind you of the best way to learn to spell. You should follow this when you are learning each word.

- **Recording your Scores**

  At the back of the book, you will find a grid for recording your scores for each unit. This will help you to keep track of how you are improving with your spelling.

- **How to Become a Better Speller**

  1. *Have a go!*
     Write the word on the piece of paper.
     Does it look right? If it doesn't look right, try writing it another way.
  2. *Look around your classroom*
     There are probably many words around you that you just didn't notice.
  3. *Use a dictionary*
     Try using a dictionary before you ask a teacher.
  4. *Ask the teacher*
     If you have tried the first three, then ask a teacher for help.

Contents

List Words	Test 1	Test 2	Test 3	Test 4	Test 5	T
climate						
chocolate						
pirate						
separate						
celebrate						
bandage						
luggage						
passage						
brigade						
trade						
parade						
paste						
mistake						
scale						
arrange						
exchange						
phrase						
disgrace						
amaze						
ashamed						
swift						
swept						

Look

Say

Cover

Write

Check

Difficult Words I Have Found	Test 1	Test 2	Test 3	T

Word Challenge

1. Make as many words as you can from the word in the box. You can rearrange the letters.

mistake

____

____

____

____

____

____

Number of words: [   ]

Small Words

2. Write a list word which contains these small words.

(a) take ______________

(b) shame ______________

(c) band ______________

(d) range ______________

(e) maze ______________

(f) grace ______________

(g) change ______________

(h) age ______________

(i) ate ______________

3. Use list words to solve the crossword.

across

1. A weighing machine
5. The fire ________ rushed to the accident
6. To place in order
7. To split up
10. To remember someone with a party or ceremony
12. A group of words
14. The yearly weather
17. Used to cover a wound
18. To surprise
19. To glue or stick
20. Error

down

2. Baggage
3. A corridor
4. The state of being in dishonour
6. The feeling of shame
8. An ocean-going bandit
9. Swap
11. To buy and sell
13. Moving with great speed
14. A sweet food
15. Past tense of 'sweep'
16. A march, usually for public display

Alphabetical Order

4. Write the list words that end in 'ge' in alphabetical order. (5)

____

____

____

____

____

Spelling Challenges

1. Write the words using look, say, cover, write, check.
2. Sort the revision words according to the number of consonants.
3. Write true or false statements using the list words.
4. Choose eight list words. Use a dictionary and write a definition for each word.

All Mixed Up

5. Unjumble these list words.

(a) spagesa ______ (b) ragibed ______
(c) gaxehecn ______ (d) lothocace ______
(e) dreapa ______ (f) gridasec ______
(g) raspetea ______ (h) fitsw ______
(i) litacem ______ (j) glagegu ______
(k) raganer ______ (l) pewts ______

Antonyms

6. Find a list or revision word with an opposite meaning.

(a) impure ______ (b) proud ______
(c) smooth ______ (d) unswept ______
(e) slow ______ (f) unknown ______
(g) honour ______ (h) attached ______

Synonyms

7. Find a list or revision word with a similar meaning.

(a) defend ______ (b) barter ______
(c) hallway ______ (d) let ______
(e) well-known ______ (f) swap ______
(g) humiliated ______ (h) prize ______

Word Worm

8. Cross out every second letter. The leftover letters will make three list words.

______ ______ ______

List

climate
chocolate
pirate
separate
celebrate
bandage
luggage
passage
brigade
trade
parade
paste
mistake
scale
arrange
exchange
phrase
disgrace
amaze
ashamed
swift
swept

Revision

stage
deal
tribe
beef
herd
deaf
aim
allow
pure
wrap
knit
calf
marble
tow
pour
famous
rough
reward
space
sailor
protect
occur

9. **Find these list words in the word search.**

climate	scale
chocolate	arrange
celebrate	exchange
bandage	separate
luggage	phrase
brigade	disgrace
trade	amaze
parade	ashamed
paste	swift
mistake	swept

g	c	e	e	k	a	t	s	i	m	c	o	s
g	p	l	e	l	a	c	s	e	b	l	d	w
e	h	u	i	g	d	a	a	t	r	i	i	i
t	r	g	e	m	n	m	z	s	i	m	s	f
a	a	g	b	b	a	n	d	a	g	e	g	t
r	s	a	p	z	b	t	t	p	a	t	r	x
b	e	g	e	s	r	e	e	a	d	e	a	d
e	g	e	a	a	m	d	b	r	e	t	c	e
l	l	u	d	t	e	a	e	c	l	p	e	m
e	e	e	k	a	r	r	a	n	g	e	s	a
c	h	o	c	o	l	a	t	e	e	w	c	h
m	e	t	a	r	a	p	e	s	l	s	l	s
e	x	c	h	a	n	g	e	t	f	s	e	a

Missing Words

10. **Use list words to complete the sentences.**

(a) They waited in the dark ready to ________________ at the surprise birthday party.

(b) The ________________ cake recipe said to ________________ the egg white from the yolk.

(c) Remember to ________________ a lift to football practice tonight.

(d) He can ________________ his books at the library.

(e) The girl found her ________________ by reading through her calculations again.

(f) Their ________________ was packed with clothes suitable for a warm ________________.

(g) The fire ________________ was ready to ________________ its engines along the street.

Incorrect Words

11. **Write these words correctly.**

(a) choclate ________________

(b) bandige ________________

(c) seperate ________________

(d) frase ________________

(e) luggige ________________

(f) disgrase ________________

(g) passige ________________

(h) brigaed ________________

(i) celibrate ________________

(j) skale ________________

UNIT 2

List Words	Test 1	Test 2	Test 3	Test 4	Test 5	T
aloud						
account						
sour						
surround						
bound						
boundary						
lounge						
trousers						
wound						
splendid						
seldom						
seek						
speech						
freedom						
freeze						
breeze						
queer						
indeed						
coffee						
geese						
skill						
sandwich						

Look Say Cover Write Check

Difficult Words I Have Found	Test 1	Test 2	Test 3	T

Small Words

1. Write the list words which contain these small words.

(a) free

____

____

(b) loud

____

(c) did

____

(d) sand

____

(e) count

____

(f) lend

____

(g) bound

____

____

Mirror Writing

2. These list words have been written in mirror writing. Can you work them out?

(a) sour ______________

(b) seek ______________

(c) skill ______________

(d) aloud ______________

3. Use list words to solve the crossword.

across

1. To turn into ice
3. To look for
4. To relax
6. Speak so it can be heard
8. Having a sharp taste, like acid
11. An article of clothing
16. A type of drink
17. Really
18. An ability to do something very well

down

1. Liberty
2. Border
3. Hardly ever
5. A jump or leap
6. A bill for payment
7. Weird
8. Encircle
9. An injury
10. Made with bread
12. Brilliant; gorgeous; magnificent
13. Talk
14. Plural of goose
15. A light wind

Adding Endings

4. Choose an ending to add to these list words.

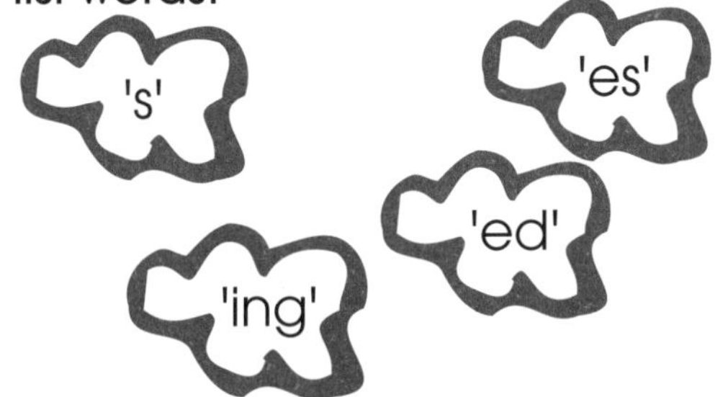

(a) skill ______________________

(b) freeze ______________________

(c) wound ______________________

(d) speech ______________________

(e) surround ______________________

(f) sandwich ______________________

Spelling Challenges

1. Write the words using look, say, cover, write, check.
2. Write the revision list in alphabetical order.
3. Give each letter in the alphabet a number; for example, a = 1, b = 2, c = 3.
4. Which list words have the highest value? For example, seek = 19 + 5 + 5 + 11 = 40

My Meanings

5. Write a definition for each of these words. Use a dictionary to check your answers.

   (a) sour ____

   ____

   (b) boundary ____

   ____

   (c) freedom ____

   ____

   (d) seldom ____

   ____

Antonyms

6. Find a list or revision word with an opposite meaning.

   (a) melt ____________ (b) often ____________

   (c) captivity ____________ (d) anxious ____________

   (e) silently ____________ (f) behind ____________

Synonyms

7. Find a list or revision word with a similar meaning.

   (a) thieve ____________ (b) approaching ____________

   (c) unsafe ____________ (d) wonderful ____________

   (e) hard ____________ (f) sharp ____________

   (g) away ____________ (h) prosper ____________

Homonyms

8. Circle the correct word.

   (a) I become very nervous when reading (aloud, allowed) in front of the class.

   (b) My young sister isn't (aloud, allowed) to ride her bike on the road.

List

aloud
account
sour
surround
bound
boundary
lounge
trousers
wound
splendid
seldom
seek
speech
freedom
freeze
breeze
queer
indeed
coffee
geese
skill
sandwich

Revision

state
steal
tide
cheer
perhaps
ahead
aid
growl
figure
written
knee
calm
purple
pillow
fourth
dangerous
tough
towards
spade
decide
absent
succeed

9. Find these list words in the word search.

aloud	indeed
account	queer
sour	freedom
surround	breeze
bound	freeze
lounge	coffee
trousers	skill
wound	splendid
seek	seldom
speech	sandwich

a	s	k	i	l	l	a	l	o	b	d	f	r
e	o	m	o	d	l	e	s	u	r	q	b	e
z	h	s	r	o	u	s	p	e	e	c	h	d
e	c	e	e	f	f	o	c	g	e	u	r	o
e	i	t	t	r	a	e	w	n	z	e	e	m
r	w	r	n	w	c	g	o	u	e	r	e	o
f	d	o	u	o	d	n	u	o	r	r	u	s
d	n	u	o	b	c	n	n	l	b	u	q	t
c	a	s	c	d	o	u	d	d	u	o	l	a
e	s	e	c	s	u	o	l	o	f	s	f	u
d	s	r	a	s	p	l	e	n	d	i	d	v
i	p	s	e	e	k	f	r	e	e	d	o	m
l	i	n	d	e	e	d	n	u	e	f	f	h

Memory Master

10. Cover the list words. Write three from memory.

_______________ _______________ _______________

Write an interesting sentence using all three words.

____

____

Word Hunt

11. Find all the list and revision words that have these sound patterns.

(a) ou (house)

(b) ee (tree)

List Words	Test 1	Test 2	Test 3	Test 4	Test 5	T
missile						
umpire						
excite						
polite						
unite						
alive						
advise						
exercise						
roam						
throat						
limb						
scratch						
snatch						
hatch						
pitch						
switch						
project						
product						
tropics						
donkey						
machine						
rubbish						

Look Say Cover Write Check

Difficult Words I Have Found	Test 1	Test 2	Test 3	T

Missing Letters

1. Complete these list words.

(a) ___n___t___

____

(b) p___ ___i ___ ___

____

(c) ___ ___ ___oa___

____

(d) l___ ___b

____

(e) d___n___ ___y

____

(f) e___ ___i___e

____

(g) ___li___ ___

____

(h) s___ ___a___ ___h

____

(i) p___t___h

____

Alphabetical Order

2. Write the list and revision words that contain 'ch' in alphabetical order. (7)

____

____

____

____

____

____

____

3. Use list words to solve the crossword.

across

1. To guide or help
7. To throw a baseball
8. A self-propelled bomb
9. A type of small doorway
10. Well-mannered
12. Stir up feelings
15. Wander
17. You __________ an itch
18. A mechanical appliance
19. An animal similar to a horse
20. The warmer parts of the world

down

1. Not dead
2. To grab rudely
3. Used to turn a light on and off
4. Bring together
5. Where your tonsils are
6. Referee
7. Something planned or proposed
11. A leg or an arm
13. Physical action to get fit
14. Waste
16. Something produced

Spelling Challenges

1. Write the list words using look, say, cover, write, check.
2. Write the list words in reverse alphabetical order.
3. Write a meaningful sentence containing three of the list words.
4. Choose five list words. Write each word in a question.

Syllable Match

4. Match the syllables to make list words.

(a)	mis •	• ite	________
(b)	pol •	• ject	________
(c)	trop •	• bish	________
(d)	pro •	• ics	________
(e)	don •	• sile	________
(f)	rub •	• key	________
(g)	pro •	• chine	________
(h)	ma •	• duct	________

All Mixed Up

5. Unjumble the list words.

(a) portics ______ (b) slimesi ______
(c) lotipe ______ (d) chartsc ______
(e) primue ______ (f) cetixe ______
(g) htach ______ (h) blim ______
(i) rothat ______ (j) vasedi ______
(k) kedoyn ______ (l) doctupr ______

Antonyms

6. Find a list or revision word with an opposite meaning.

(a) lost ______
(b) impolite ______
(c) dead ______
(d) separate ______

Synonyms

7. Find a list or revision word with a similar meaning.

(a) easy ______ (b) misplace ______
(c) thin ______ (d) incorrect ______
(e) grab ______ (f) garbage ______

Adding Endings

8. Complete this table of suffixes.

	word	add 's'	add 'd'	add 'ing'
(a)	advise	advises	advised	advising
(b)	excite			
(c)	exercise			
(d)	umpire			
(e)	promise			
(f)	notice			
(g)	unite			

List

missile
umpire
excite
polite
unite
alive
advise
exercise
roam
throat
limb
scratch
snatch
hatch
pitch
switch
project
product
tropics
donkey
machine
rubbish

Revision

escape
steam
found
agree
interest
thread
paid
drown
capture
wrong
ugly
grasp
simple
narrow
sigh
enter
search
nineteen
blade
cabin
lose
reply

9. Find these list words in the word search.

throat	hatch
missile	pitch
umpire	switch
excite	donkey
polite	machine
unite	tropics
advise	rubbish
alive	project
exercise	product
scratch	limb
roam	

u	n	e	s	i	v	d	a	e	x	e	s	h
e	e	n	i	h	c	a	m	e	c	b	t	a
i	t	n	m	a	o	r	r	s	p	m	c	x
t	a	l	i	v	e	l	u	i	r	i	u	e
p	o	l	i	t	e	o	b	c	o	l	d	r
i	r	h	c	t	a	h	b	r	j	c	o	i
t	h	t	t	p	e	c	i	e	e	e	r	p
c	t	r	h	i	l	t	s	x	c	t	p	m
h	c	o	r	s	i	a	h	e	t	i	n	u
s	w	a	c	c	d	r	o	a	p	c	n	m
l	t	r	o	p	i	c	s	s	p	x	a	i
i	m	b	m	m	i	s	s	i	l	e	c	h
s	w	i	t	c	h	b	y	e	k	n	o	d

Magic Words

10. Change the first word into the last by changing one letter on each line to make a new word.

For example:

limb
lime
time
tame
tape

(a) roam	(b) paid
herd	fell

More Than One

11. Complete this table of plurals.

	Word	Add 's' or 'es'
(a)	limb	
(b)	hatch	
(c)	umpire	
(d)	scratch	
(e)	product	
(f)	missile	

Two Meanings

12. The list word 'limb' has more than one meaning. Write two sentences to show the difference.

(a) ______________________________

____

____

(b) ______________________________

____

____

UNIT 4

List Words	Test 1	Test 2	Test 3	Test 4	Test 5	T
treat						
repeat						
beneath						
seam						
spear						
appear						
shear						
weary						
weave						
disease						
increase						
peace						
plastic						
elastic						
contest						
construct						
district						
stomach						
instant						
cliff						
bury						
facsimile						

Look Say Cover Write Check

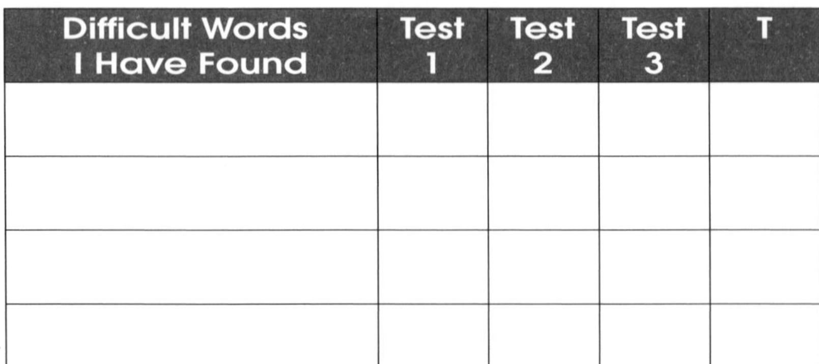

Difficult Words I Have Found	Test 1	Test 2	Test 3	T

Word Worm

1. (a) Circle each list word you can find in the word worm.

(b) Write the eight list words that are not in the word worm.

Seam
beneath
stomach
districh
facsmile
increase
construct
weary

Anagrams

2. Rearrange the letters in each of these list or revision words to make a new word.
For example, spear – pears

(a) seam Meas
(b) bury ruby
(c) smile limes

3. Use list words to solve the crossword.

across

2. A join in clothing
3. A particular area, region or locality
5. Competition
6. A reward
10. A weapon
11. To move from side to side
13. To cut wool from a sheep
14. Freedom from war
15. To put beneath the earth
16. A steep, rocky slope
18. An exact copy
20. The part of the body that digests food
21. To build

down

1. Under
4. Opposite of decrease
7. To do it again
8. Illness
9. Opposite of disappear
12. Tired
14. Your lunch is in the __________ bag
17. Immediate
19. Springy

Alphabetical Order

4. Put all the list words that contain the 'ea' sound into alphabetical order. (12)

____

____

____

____

Spelling Challenges

1. Write the list words using look, say, cover, write, check.
2. Write the revision list in alphabetical order.
3. Write five silly sentences. You must use all of the list words within those five sentences.
4. Jumble each revision word. Give to a friend to unjumble.

UNIT 4

Missing Words

5. **Use list words to complete the sentences.**

(a) They were told to ______________ a bridge using only straws and tape.

(b) The camera was able to take ______________ photographs.

(c) The children were sure that their model had won the ______________ for their school ______________.

(d) The ______________ was stretched across the ______________ bottle to explain pitch.

(e) The children went fishing ______________ the pier that was near the rocky ______________.

(f) ______________ the experiment at two o'clock every day and ______________ the plants with great care.

Antonyms

6. **Find a list or revision word with an opposite meaning.**

(a) tight ______________ (b) demolish ______________

(c) war ______________ (d) decrease ______________

Synonyms

7. **Find a list or revision word with a similar meaning.**

(a) tired ______________ (b) under ______________

(c) sickness ______________ (d) wood ______________

(e) build ______________ (f) eager ______________

Homonyms

8. **Circle the correct word.**

(a) Learning something new may (seem, seam) difficult at first, so you must persevere.

(b) It is difficult to hand sew through a thick (seem, seam) on a pair of jeans.

(c) There has seldom been a time in the past when the world was at (piece, peace).

(d) It is best to vacuum the floor thoroughly after breaking a glass to ensure that every (piece, peace) is gone.

List

treat
repeat
beneath
seam
spear
appear
shear
weary
weave
disease
increase
peace
plastic
elastic
contest
construct
district
stomach
instant
cliff
bury
facsimile

Revision

shape
scream
smile
keen
western
spread
pain
crown
nature
edge
copy
believe
candle
fellow
ninety
sigh
timber
pearl
blaze
basin
loose
ourselves

9. Find these list words in the word search.

seam	disease
treat	stomach
spear	plastic
repeat	instant
beneath	elastic
appear	construct
weary	district
shear	cliff
weave	bury
peace	increase

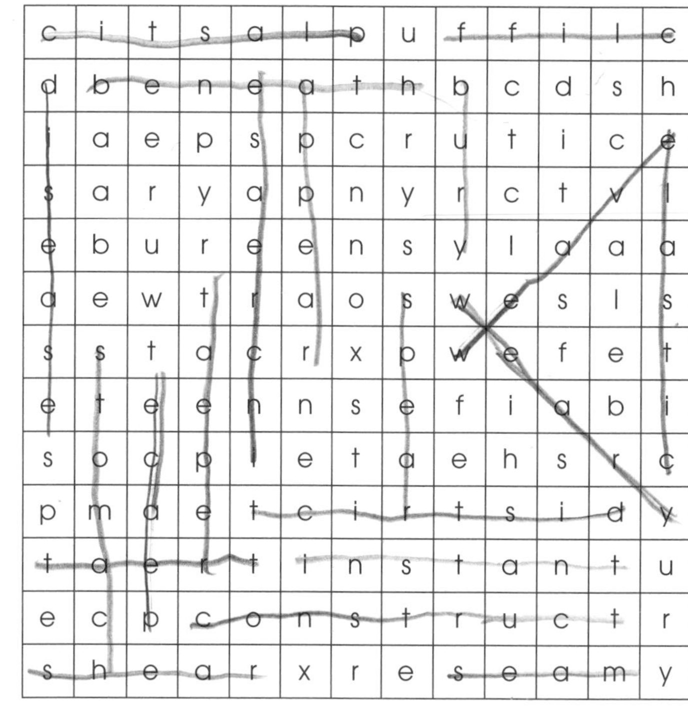

c	i	t	s	a	l	p	u	f	f	i	l	e
d	b	e	n	e	a	t	h	b	c	d	s	h
i	a	e	p	s	p	c	r	u	t	i	c	e
s	a	r	y	a	p	n	y	r	c	t	v	l
e	b	u	r	e	e	n	s	y	l	a	a	a
a	e	w	t	r	a	o	s	w	e	s	l	s
s	s	t	a	c	r	x	p	w	e	f	e	t
e	t	e	e	n	n	s	e	f	i	a	b	i
s	o	c	p	i	e	t	a	e	h	s	r	c
p	m	a	e	t	c	i	r	t	s	i	d	y
t	a	e	r	t	i	n	s	t	a	n	t	u
e	c	p	c	o	n	s	t	r	u	c	t	r
s	h	e	a	r	x	r	e	s	e	a	m	y

Shape Sorter

10. Match each shape with a list or revision word.

(a) 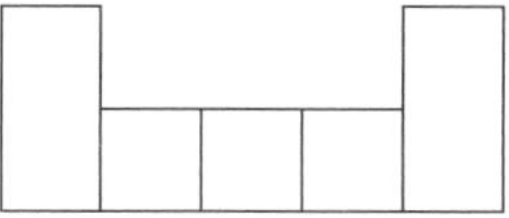

(b) 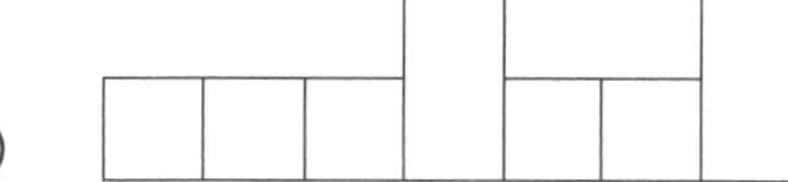

(c) 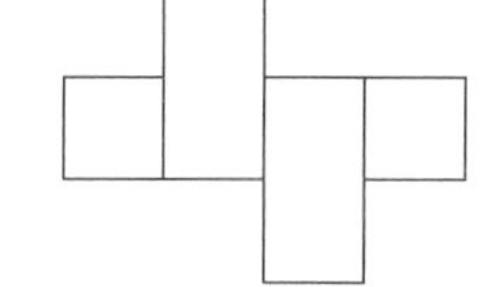

(d) 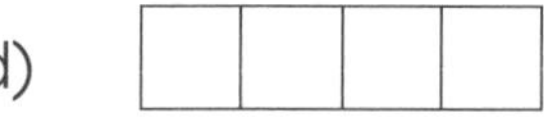

(e) 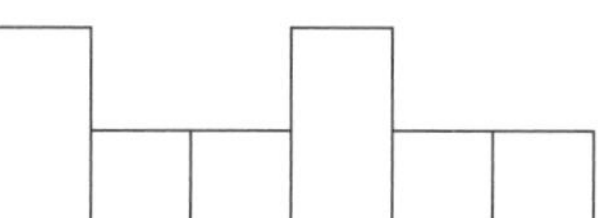

(f) 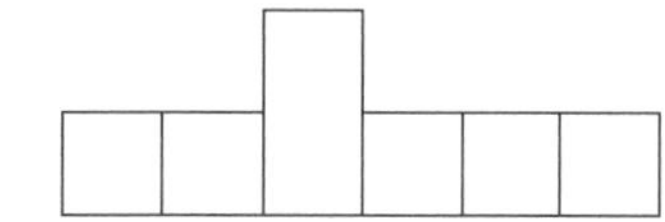

(g) 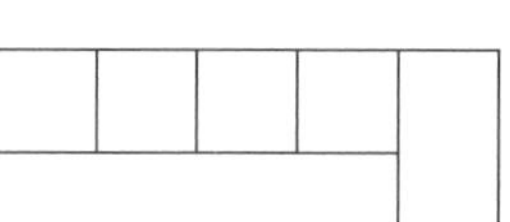

(h) 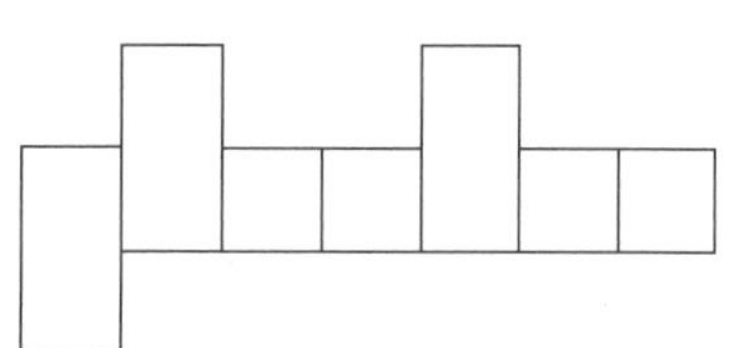

Memory Master

11. Cover the list words. Write three from memory.

__________ __________ __________

Write a question using all three words.

List Words	Test 1	Test 2	Test 3	Test 4	Test 5	T
cherry						
berry						
hobby						
navy						
enemy						
holy						
immediately						
industry						
admit						
splash						
shelter						
waist						
obtain						
contain						
complain						
explain						
brain						
jail						
daily						
tailor						
tadpole						
supply						

Look Say Cover Write Check

Difficult Words I Have Found	Test 1	Test 2	Test 3	T

Mirror Writing

1. These list words have been written in mirror writing. Can you work them out?

(a) hsalqs ____________

(b) liaj ____________

(c) niatnoc ____________

(d) ylppus ____________

(e) timda ____________

(f) niarb ____________

Compound Words

2. Match the words to make compound words.

____

____

____

____

3. Use list words to solve the crossword.

across

2. Opposite of friend
6. A small, red fruit
7. Agriculture is a large ________ in Australia and the USA
9. An enjoyable pastime
14. The sound made by something hitting the water
16. A person who makes clothes
18. To get
19. To provide
21. A part of your body between your ribs and hips
22. To give reasons for

down

1. Now
3. A country's warships
4. Confess
5. A small juicy fruit
8. Sacred to religion
10. Found in the head
11. To enclose or include
12. Another word for prison
13. Cover
15. The name given to a frog after it develops from an egg
17. To state a grievance
20. Happening every day

Jumbled Words

4. Two list words have been jumbled together in each example below. Write the two list words you find.

(a) heemyolyn

________ + ________

(b) basippunyrl

________ + ________

(c) betirwarsy

________ + ________

(d) toralnaivy

________ + ________

Spelling Challenges

1. Write the list words using look, say, cover, write, check.
2. Write the revision list in reverse alphabetical order.
3. Write the list words according to your own rule. Can a friend guess the rule?
4. Choose eight list words. Write a meaningful sentence for each word.

All Mixed Up

5. Unjumble the list words.

(a) vany ______ (b) plusyp ______
(c) sutinydr ______ (d) plinomac ______
(e) rabin ______ (f) stwai ______
(g) ainbot ______ (h) rebry ______
(i) tamid ______ (j) letsher ______
(k) recyhr ______ (l) yeenm ______

Antonyms

6. Find a list or revision word with an opposite meaning.

(a) delayed ______ (b) specific ______
(c) fancy ______ (d) deny ______
(e) ally ______ (f) unpleasant ______

Synonyms

7. Find a list or revision word similar in meaning.

(a) foe ______ (b) whine ______
(c) prison ______ (d) pastime ______
(e) torment ______ (f) now ______

Homonyms

8. Circle the correct word.

(a) Many factories cause major pollution problems by allowing (waist, waste) products to flow straight into the ocean.

(b) Clothes can become very uncomfortable if they're too tight around your (waist, waste).

(c) We enjoyed visiting a (berry, bury) farm when we went to the country.

(d) Dogs love to (berry, bury) their bones in a particular place in the garden.

(e) Mum and Dad were not (wholly, holy) in agreement with allowing me to camp the night in a tent at a friend's house.

(f) The Bible is a (wholly, holy) book.

List

cherry
berry
hobby
navy
enemy
holy
immediately
industry
admit
splash
shelter
waist
obtain
contain
complain
explain
brain
jail
daily
tailor
tadpole
supply

Revision

shave
tease
network
sixteen
general
pleasant
plain
March
adventure
hedge
study
thief
handle
borrow
January
burnt
thunder
chance
tour
comb
lonely
poem

9. Find these list words in the word search.

cherry	obtain
berry	contain
hobby	complain
navy	explain
enemy	brain
holy	jail
supply	daily
immediately	tailor
industry	waist
admit	splash

e	r	d	f	x	g	b	r	a	i	n	a	h
y	o	x	r	w	q	y	y	x	r	i	d	y
e	l	k	c	a	t	l	n	l	l	a	m	i
v	i	e	q	v	o	p	i	q	p	l	i	n
s	a	h	t	h	t	p	a	v	k	p	t	d
r	t	s	q	a	l	u	l	k	l	m	u	u
n	l	a	u	p	i	s	p	d	e	o	m	s
i	j	l	m	j	y	d	x	n	a	c	l	t
a	i	p	a	r	o	p	e	n	b	i	c	r
t	c	s	r	c	z	m	a	m	a	n	l	y
n	b	e	r	r	y	v	a	j	m	e	o	y
o	h	o	b	b	y	p	i	w	a	i	s	t
c	v	c	o	d	d	o	b	t	a	i	n	r

Alphabetical Order

10. Put the list words that end with 'y' into alphabetical order. (10)

____

____

____

Adding Endings

11. (a) Follow the pattern to make these words plural.

(i) hobby hobbies

(ii) enemy ______________

(iii) cherry ______________

(iv) navy ______________

(v) berry ______________

(vi) industry ______________

(vii) supply ______________

(b) Write the rule for changing words that end in 'y' into plurals.

____

____

____

Word Challenge

12. Make as many words as you can from the word in the box. You can rearrange the letters.

explain

____

____

____

____

Unit 6

List Words	Test 1	Test 2	Test 3	Test 4	Test 5	T
death						
breath						
heaven						
meant						
feather						
wealth						
palace						
adult						
adopt						
pupil						
tennis						
linen						
limit						
wedding						
truth						
honest						
practice						
intend						
inspect						
fond						
final						
vessel						

Look Say Cover Write Check

Difficult Words I Have Found	Test 1	Test 2	Test 3	T

Word Worm

1. Cross out every second letter. The leftover letters will make three list words.

____

____

____

Small Words

2. Write a list word which contains these small words.

(a) mean ______________

(b) ten ______________

(c) nest ______________

(d) lace ______________

(e) at ______________

(f) in ______________

(g) me ______________

(h) he ______________

(i) her ______________

3. Use list words to solve the crossword.

across

3. I found a bird's __________ on the ground
6. Opposite of birth
7. The end point
9. A grown-up person
12. Opposite of hell
14. Student
16. End
17. Opposite of dishonest
18. A marriage ceremony
20. To look closely at
21. A synonym for ship

down

1. Past tense of 'to mean'
2. A game played with a ball and racket
4. Opposite of falsehood
5. The air taken in and given out of the lungs
8. Take on
10. The home of a king or queen
11. Riches
13. The business of a doctor or dentist
15. A type of cloth
16. To like something
19. To mean

Two Meanings

4. The list word 'pupil' has more than one meaning. Write two sentences to show the difference.

(a) ______________________________

____

____

(b) ______________________________

____

____

Spelling Challenges

1. Write the list words using look, say, cover, write, check.
2. Sort the list words according to the number of syllables.
3. Write the revision words in alphabetical order.
4. Make word shapes for each list word.

Missing Words

5. Use list or revision words to complete the sentences.

(a) It was so cold on the deck of the ________________, the boy could see his own ________________.

(b) The school ________________ wrote a poem about a bird's ________________.

(c) She was very ________________ of the white ________________ dress.

(d) They ________________ to put up a fence before the new dog arrives.

(e) The owners were coming to ________________ the house for the ________________ time.

(f) They decided to ________________ a new system for lending books that would ________________ borrowing to five books a week.

Antonyms

6. Find a list or revision word with an opposite meaning.

(a) lies ________________ (b) life ________________

(c) pain ________________ (d) first ________________

(e) poverty ________________ (f) dishonest ________________

Synonyms

7. Find a list or revision word similar in meaning.

(a) idle ________________ (b) last ________________

(c) student ________________ (d) guardian ________________

(e) ship ________________ (f) trunk ________________

Homonyms

8. Circle the correct word.

(a) You have to (practice, practise) hard to play a musical instrument well.

(b) Our doctor sold his (practice, practise) to another doctor.

List

death
breath
heaven
meant
feather
wealth
palace
adult
adopt
pupil
tennis
linen
limit
wedding
truth
honest
practice
intend
inspect
fond
final
vessel

Revision

slave
millimetre
pile
sneeze
capital
pleasure
remain
crowd
postage
lazy
porridge
tomato
jungle
arrow
February
parent
rather
chance
cursor
crumb
chest
gang

9. Find these list words in the word search.

death	tennis
breath	linen
heaven	limit
meant	wedding
feather	vessel
wealth	truth
palace	honest
adult	intend
adopt	inspect
pupil	fond
final	

d	i	n	s	p	e	c	t	a	w	m	t	t
o	e	x	f	k	u	v	d	l	c	n	i	e
v	e	a	h	o	n	e	s	t	s	e	m	n
y	u	d	t	n	a	e	m	b	t	n	i	n
i	e	u	a	h	e	a	v	e	n	i	l	i
z	c	l	e	d	r	p	u	p	i	l	f	s
g	j	t	r	e	h	t	a	e	f	e	i	m
n	u	n	b	g	d	p	f	l	q	u	n	l
i	t	a	b	n	t	p	o	d	a	w	a	e
d	m	l	o	g	c	r	o	h	h	c	l	s
d	r	f	a	e	r	i	u	q	u	y	e	s
e	d	e	d	j	k	i	n	t	e	n	d	e
w	e	a	l	t	h	u	p	y	h	o	x	v

Missing Letters

10. Complete these list and revision words.

(a) f____ ____th____ ____

(b) w____dd____ ____ ____

(c) a____ ____p____

(d) ____on____ ____t

(e) d____ ____t____

(f) m____a____t

(g) p____p____ ____

(h) p____l____ ____e

(i) in____ ____ ____ct

(j) ____ ____ss____l

(k) ____ ____ea____h

(l) w____ ____lth

Word Hunt

11. Write all the list and revision words that contain a double consonant.
For example, te**nn**is.

________________ ________________

________________ ________________

________________ ________________

Memory Master

12. Cover the list words.
Write three from memory.

____

____

____

Write an interesting sentence that contains all three words.

____

____

____

____

____

List Words	Test 1	Test 2	Test 3	Test 4	Test 5	T
dawn						
awful						
law						
synthetic						
prevent						
problem						
attack						
traffic						
result						
length						
fact						
orchard						
starch						
harvest						
partner						
pardon						
alarm						
bargain						
carpenter						
standard						
regular						
sense						

Look

Say

Cover

Write

Check

Difficult Words I Have Found	Test 1	Test 2	Test 3	T

Shape Sorter

1. Match each shape with a list word.

(a) 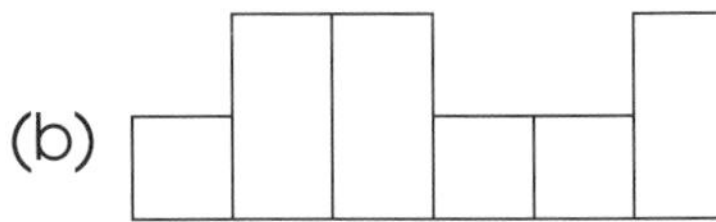

(b) 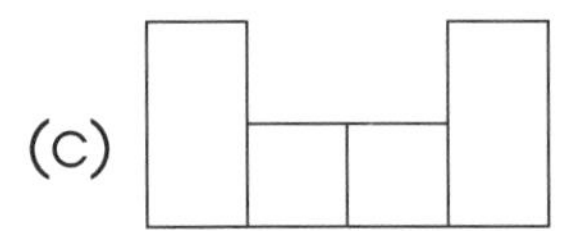

(c) 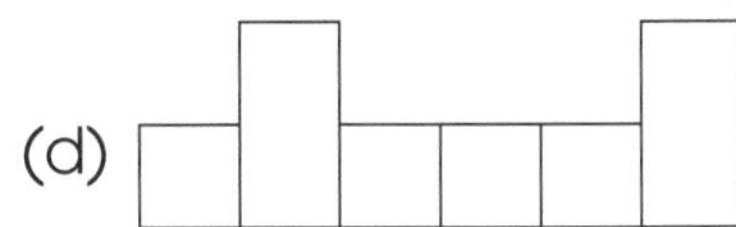

(d) 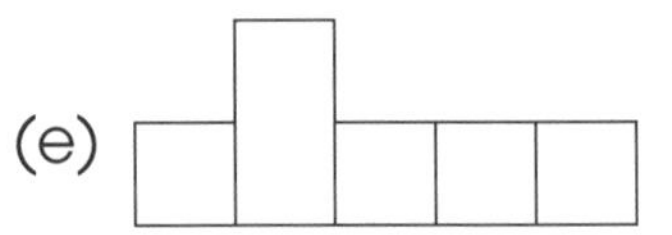

(e) 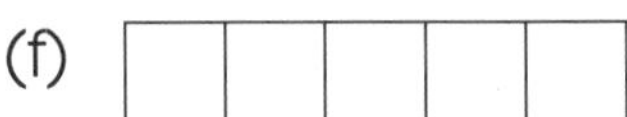

(f)

(g) 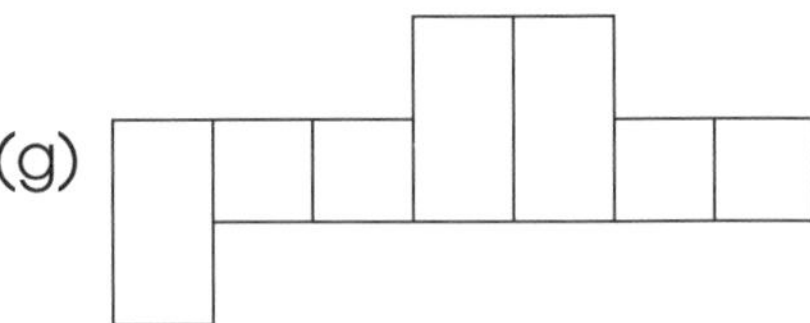

Word Meanings

2. Write the list word that matches each meaning.

(a) first light in the morning

____

(b) a person who makes things out of wood

____

(c) a place where fruit trees grow

____

(d) something that is true or real

____

3. Use list words to solve the crossword.

across

4. A garden of fruit trees
6. Opposite of fiction
8. Something bought at a cheap price
10. Terrible
11. Formed from unnatural origins
12. Forgive
13. To stop something from happening
15. A level aimed at
17. To gather crops
19. How long something is
20. A person who works with wood

down

1. Used to make clothing stiff
2. The beginning of the day
3. Assault
5. Outcome
7. The rules of a country
9. Frighten
12. Companion
13. Something which has to be solved
14. There was a ___________ jam on the motorway
16. Opposite of irregular
18. Your nose gives you your ___________ of smell

Alphabetical Order

4. Put the list words that contain the 'ar' sound in alphabetical order. (10)

____

____

____

____

____

____

Spelling Challenges

1. Write the list words using look, say, cover, write, check.
2. Write true or false statements using the revision words.
3. Make word sums for the list words. For example, har + vest = harvest
4. Write the revision list in reverse alphabetical order.

UNIT 7

All Mixed Up

5. Unjumble the list words.

(a) ralam ______ (b) lurgera ______

(c) graniba ______ (d) wand ______

(e) bompler ______ (f) verpetn ______

(g) drastand ______ (h) tacf ______

(i) chodarr ______ (j) tacakt ______

(k) selrut ______ (l) natperr ______

Antonyms

6. Find a list or revision word with an opposite meaning.

(a) misbehave ______ (b) intermittent ______

(c) defend ______ (d) improper ______

Synonyms

7. Find a list or revision word with a similar meaning.

(a) mark ______ (b) cost ______

(c) avoid ______ (d) terrible ______

(e) unite ______ (f) negotiate ______

(g) forgive ______ (h) goods ______

My Meanings

8. Write a definition for each of these words.
Use a dictionary to check your answers.

(a) bargain ______

______

______

(b) harvest ______

______

(c) law ______

______

(d) synthetic ______

______

List

dawn
awful
law
synthetic
prevent
problem
attack
traffic
result
length
fact
orchard
starch
harvest
partner
pardon
alarm
bargain
carpenter
standard
regular
sense

Revision

behave
centimetre
price
join
stem
treasure
stain
powder
cabbage
electric
dairy
potato
bubble
except
October
moment
proper
balance
roast
cargo
chew
suit

9. Find these list words in the word search.

dawn	awful
law	fact
orchard	starch
regular	harvest
prevent	partner
problem	pardon
sense	alarm
attack	bargain
traffic	carpenter
result	standard

p	t	r	a	f	f	i	c	c	e	q	o	d
r	a	a	p	d	k	c	a	t	t	a	a	r
e	p	r	o	b	l	e	m	r	o	w	a	f
v	r	p	d	u	y	e	i	n	n	f	d	o
e	a	z	q	o	g	i	r	e	s	u	l	t
n	l	u	m	y	n	a	i	r	e	l	a	w
t	u	n	i	a	g	r	a	b	h	x	l	t
b	g	f	a	c	t	e	s	o	s	w	a	s
m	e	x	u	v	e	n	t	t	i	y	r	e
d	r	a	d	n	a	t	s	t	a	e	m	v
k	w	u	o	j	o	r	c	h	a	r	d	r
s	e	n	s	e	k	a	t	a	u	e	c	a
v	a	l	c	a	r	p	e	n	t	e	r	h

Adding Endings

10. Add 'ing' to these words.

	word	add 'ing'
(a)	attack	
(b)	balance	
(c)	alarm	
(d)	behave	
(e)	harvest	
(f)	bargain	

Memory Master

11. Cover the list words. Write three from memory.

____

____

____

Write an interesting sentence using all three words.

Extend Yourself

12. A 'carpenter' is a type of occupation. Describe these occupations.

(a) plumber

(b) teacher

UNIT 8

List Words	Test 1	Test 2	Test 3	Test 4	Test 5	T
bare						
share						
prepare						
flow						
growth						
unknown						
shadow						
swallow						
bullet						
bomb						
beyond						
surf						
surface						
burst						
turkey						
attend						
atom						
atmosphere						
angel						
shovel						
model						
object						

Look Say Cover Write Check

Difficult Words I Have Found	Test 1	Test 2	Test 3	T

Small Words

1. Write a list word which contain these small words.

(a) low ______________

(b) hare ______________

(c) bull ______________

(d) key ______________

(e) sphere ______________

(f) face ______________

(g) known ______________

(h) end ______________

Word Hunt

2. Which list words:

(a) end in 'ow'?

____

____

____

(b) can be rearranged to spell 'moat'?

____

(c) have a silent letter?

____

(d) rhyme with 'first'?

____

3. **Use list words to solve the crossword.**

across

2. An explosive device
4. A purpose or aim
5. A bird often eaten
7. The top of the water
12. Darkness made from light
13. To get ready
14. Comes from heaven
15. Uncovered
16. A type of bird
17. The gases surrounding the earth

down

1. To be present at
2. Pop! (a balloon)
3. Out of reach
6. An increase
7. Similar to spade
8. The smallest part of an element
9. Moving smoothly
10. Opposite of known
11. A copy of something but in a smaller size
12. To divide
15. Comes out of a gun
16. The foam of breaking waves

Alphabetical Order

4. **Put the list and revision words that begin with 's' in alphabetical order. (8)**

Spelling Challenges

1. Write the list words using look, say, cover, write, check.
2. Write a meaningful sentence containing each list word.
3. Write each of the revision words in a question.
4. Write a paragraph containing all of the list words.

Word Meanings

5. Write the list word that matches each meaning.

(a) an example used for copying or comparing ____________

(b) to distribute between more than one person ____________

(c) to use your body or a board to ride waves ____________

(d) a large bird bred mainly for eating ____________

(e) a winged creature ____________

(f) the air that surrounds the earth ____________

(g) a piece of metal shot from a gun ____________

(h) the smallest part ____________

Antonyms

6. Find a list or revision word with an opposite meaning.

(a) quiet ____________ (b) known ____________

(c) messy ____________ (d) light ____________

(e) full ____________ (f) covered ____________

Synonyms

7. Find a list or revision word with a similar meaning.

(a) gulp ____________ (b) spade ____________

(c) destroy ____________ (d) exterior ____________

(e) action ____________ (f) distribute ____________

Homonyms

8. Circle the correct word.

(a) A polar (bare, bear) is well camouflaged in its natural environment of ice and snow.

(b) The walls in the classroom were (bare, bear).

(c) It is very relaxing to watch a stream or a river (flow, floe) gently past.

(d) An ice (flow, floe) can be found at the North Pole.

List

bare
share
prepare
flow
growth
unknown
shadow
swallow
bullet
bomb
beyond
surf
surface
burst
turkey
attend
atom
atmosphere
angel
shovel
model
object

Revision

damage
neat
vine
noisy
silk
heavy
hail
power
ribbon
subject
empty
weigh
paddle
excuse
December
movement
grocer
distance
trunk
parcel
bench
ocean

9. Find these list words in the word search.

bare	beyond
share	surf
prepare	surface
flow	burst
growth	turkey
unknown	attend
shadow	atom
swallow	model
bullet	angel
bomb	shovel

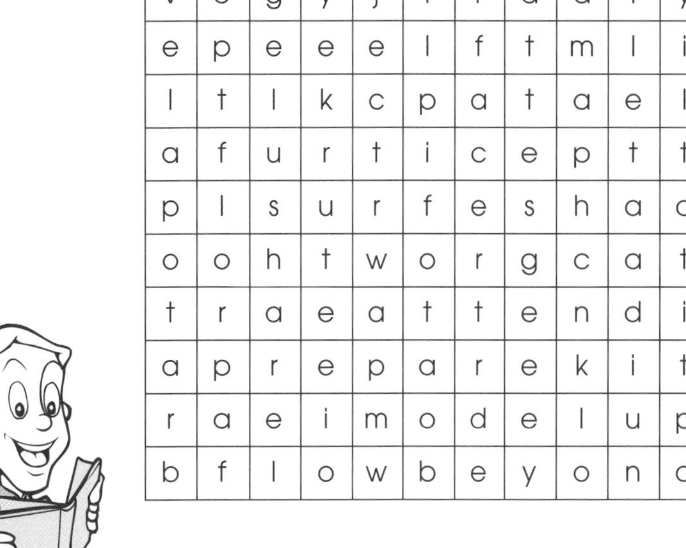

s	a	s	u	r	p	y	c	i	m	x	t	a
h	d	a	m	o	u	s	e	a	b	o	m	b
o	e	n	g	b	i	u	w	s	u	b	b	a
v	e	g	y	j	t	r	a	a	l	y	o	t
e	p	e	e	e	l	f	t	m	l	i	m	m
l	t	l	k	c	p	a	t	a	e	l	o	g
a	f	u	r	t	i	c	e	p	t	t	o	n
p	l	s	u	r	f	e	s	h	a	d	o	w
o	o	h	t	w	o	r	g	c	a	t	b	o
t	r	a	e	a	t	t	e	n	d	i	u	n
a	p	r	e	p	a	r	e	k	i	t	r	k
r	a	e	i	m	o	d	e	l	u	p	s	n
b	f	l	o	w	b	e	y	o	n	d	t	u

Silent Letters

10. Write the list words that contain a silent letter.

(a) ____________________

(b) ____________________

Think of three more words that contain a silent letter.

____

____

____

Two Meanings

11. The list word 'atmosphere' has more than one meaning. Write two sentences to show the difference.

(a) ____________________

____

____

____

(b) ____________________

____

____

____

Adding Endings

12. Complete this table of suffixes.

	word	add 's'	add 'd' or 'ed'	add 'ing'
(a)	prepare			preparing
(b)			shovelled	
(c)		models		modelling
(d)				surfacing
(e)	flow		flowed	

UNIT 9

List Words	Test 1	Test 2	Test 3	Test 4	Test 5	T
orphan						
organ						
ordinary						
sword						
afford						
record						
support						
transport						
enormous						
uniform						
factory						
decorate						
therefore						
explore						
forward						
author						
metal						
technology						
cotton						
dye						
hero						
worse						

Look

Say

Cover

Write

Check

Difficult Words I Have Found	Test 1	Test 2	Test 3	T

Jumbled Words

1. Two list words have been jumbled together in each example below. Write the two list words you find.

   (a) dofferady

   ______________ + ______________

   (b) gooharren

   ______________ + ______________

   (c) setomlardw

   ______________ + ______________

   (d) cenwosottor

   ______________ + ______________

   (e) teeloxhaurorp

   ______________ + ______________

2. Use list words to solve the crossword.

across

4. My cold is __________ today than yesterday
5. The clothes worn by a soldier
7. Knowledge to do with science and engineering
8. A building where things are made
10. A long steel weapon
12. The writer of a book
14. Have enough money to buy
16. Gives colouring to cloth
17. A child without parents
18. An old form of recording music
20. To carry or move
21. Opposite of backward

down

1. A plant from which a cloth is made
2. 'Lets __________ the Christmas tree!'
3. Very large
6. Conducts electricity
9. A person who performs brave deeds
11. Average
13. It is raining; __________ we will go inside
15. To help
17. A musical instrument
19. Investigate

Spelling Challenges

1. Write the list words using look, say, cover, write, check.
2. Make word shapes for the revision words.
3. Sort the list words according to the number of syllables.
4. Use a dictionary to write a definition for 10 list or revision words.

UNIT 9

All Mixed Up

3. Unjumble the list words.

(a) sportarnt ____________ (b) porstup ____________

(c) dwofarr ____________ (d) ridaryon ____________

(e) ploxere ____________ (f) sorwe ____________

(g) goarn ____________ (h) dorsw ____________

(i) toctno ____________ (j) dretocae ____________

(k) credor ____________ (l) forafd ____________

Missing Words

4. Use list words to complete these sentences.

(a) Can we ____________ to go bowling on the weekend?

(b) They will ____________ the furniture to the new house tomorrow.

(c) She bought candles and sweets to ____________ the birthday cake.

(d) The children wanted to ____________ the caves before it became dark.

(e) She took her favourite book to the shop to be signed by the ____________.

Homonyms

5. Circle the correct word.

(a) I will (dye, die) my hair bright orange when I go to the fancy dress party dressed as a clown.

(b) Fish will (dye, die) if unable to return to water within a short time.

Alphabetical Order

6. Put the list words that contain the 'or' sound into alphabetical order. (16)

____

____

____

____

List

orphan
organ
ordinary
sword
afford
record
support
transport
enormous
uniform
factory
decorate
therefore
explore
forward
author
metal
technology
cotton
dye
hero
worse

Revision

manage
weak
size
spoil
public
video
trail
fare
address
wage
worry
decade
battle
expect
vowel
demand
offer
ghost
flour
artist
straw
plough

7. Find these list words in the word search.

orphan	uniform
organ	factory
ordinary	decorate
forward	explore
author	worse
sword	metal
afford	record
support	cotton
transport	dye
enormous	hero

s	o	h	e	n	e	d	h	e	e	c	o	r
a	u	t	h	o	r	n	e	t	s	o	w	a
e	r	p	y	t	d	d	r	a	w	r	o	f
n	m	p	p	t	l	o	o	r	o	p	r	t
o	h	e	a	o	l	a	g	o	r	h	s	e
r	y	d	t	c	r	o	r	c	d	a	e	m
m	r	r	u	a	t	t	e	e	r	n	s	r
o	a	o	c	h	l	u	a	d	w	o	d	o
u	n	c	t	f	a	c	t	o	r	y	r	f
s	i	e	e	r	o	l	p	x	e	o	o	i
o	d	r	s	o	r	y	t	t	r	p	f	n
t	r	a	n	s	p	o	r	t	n	s	f	u
n	o	l	l	a	g	r	a	o	r	g	a	n

Memory Master

8. Cover the list words. Write three from memory.

__________ __________ __________

Write an interesting sentence using all three words.

Adding Endings

9. Add as many of the word endings as possible to the given words.

decorate decorates, decorating, decoration

record

explore

transport

support

List Words	Test 1	Test 2	Test 3	Test 4	Test 5	T
verb						
verse						
serve						
environment						
perform						
perfect						
merchant						
mineral						
several						
concert						
ambulance						
modern						
northern						
remember						
copper						
customer						
gardener						
hunger						
wander						
national						
member						
passenger						

Look

Say

Cover

Write

Check

Difficult Words I Have Found	Test 1	Test 2	Test 3	T

ɿoɿɿiM Writing

1. These list words have been written in mirror writing. Can you work them out?

(a) ɿɘqqoɔ ______________

(b) ɿɘϱnuʜ ______________

(c) ɘvɿɘƨ ______________

(d) lɒnoitɒn ______________

Now write these revision words in mirror writing.

(e) ______________ tore

(f) ______________ fail

(g) ______________ kettle

(h) ______________ scout

Small Words

2. Write a list word which contains these small words.

(a) form ______________

(b) mine ______________

(c) on ______________

(d) garden ______________

(e) ant ______________

(f) hung ______________

(g) wand ______________

(h) pass ______________

3. Use list words to solve the crossword.

across

1. A 'doing' word
3. Act
4. To give out food
5. A desire for food
7. Roam
8. Music performed in public
10. Belonging to (a club)
12. Client
13. A person who buys and sells things
16. More than one
17. Opposite of southern
18. A vehicle that carries sick or injured people
19. The surrounding things, conditions and influences

down

1. Lines of poetry
2. The train __________ fell asleep and missed his station
3. Without fault
6. A person who works in a garden
9. To do with a nation
11. A metal
13. A substance found in the earth and mined
14. Opposite of forget
15. Opposite of ancient

Word Challenge

4. Make as many words as you can from the word in the box. You can rearrange the letters.

merchant

____

____

____

____

Number of words:

Spelling Challenges

1. Write the list words using look, say, cover, write, check.
2. Sort the list words according to your own rule. Can a friend guess the rule?
3. Write five silly sentences. You must use all of the list words within the sentences.
4. Write the revision list in reverse alphabetical order.

My Meanings

5. Write a definition for each of these words. Use a dictionary to check your answers.

(a) verb ____________________

(b) verse ____________________

(c) modern ____________________

(d) environment ____________________

(e) national ____________________

(f) mineral ____________________

Antonyms

6. Find a list or revision word with an opposite meaning.

(a) succeed ____________ (b) imperfect ____________

(c) expensive ____________ (d) southern ____________

(e) forget ____________ (f) ancient ____________

Synonyms

7. Find a list or revision word with a similar meaning.

(a) act ____________ (b) gaze ____________

(c) many ____________ (d) shopper ____________

(e) unite ____________ (f) ripped ____________

Shape Sorter

8. Match each shape with a list word.

(a) 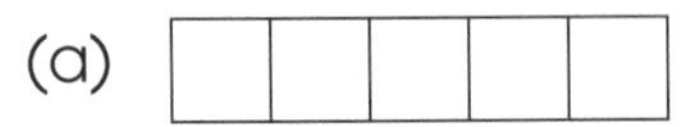

(b) 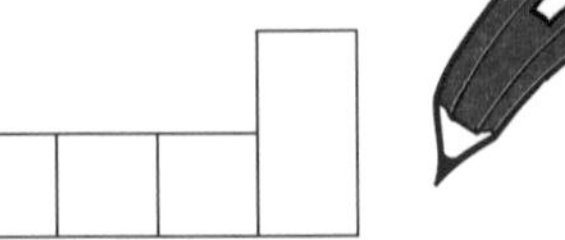

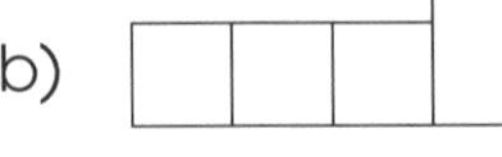

(c)

(d) 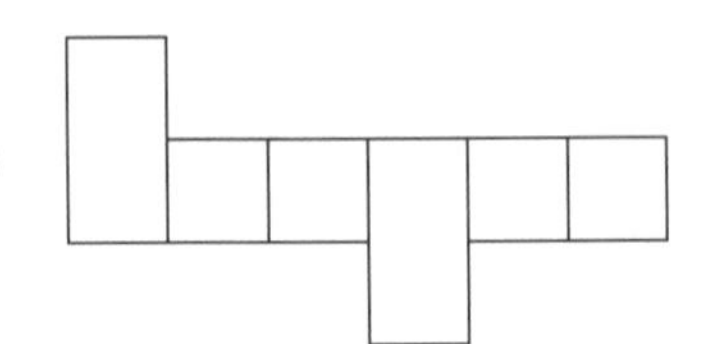

(e) 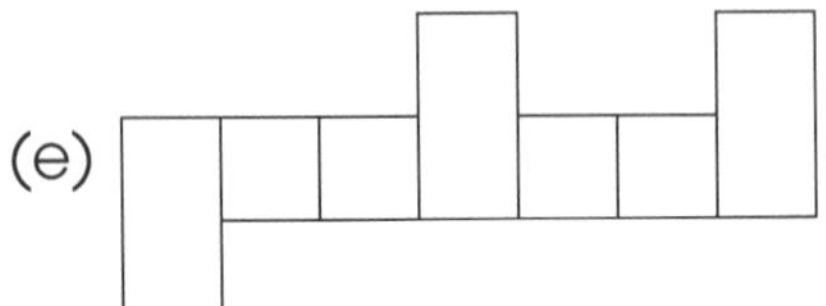

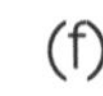

(f) 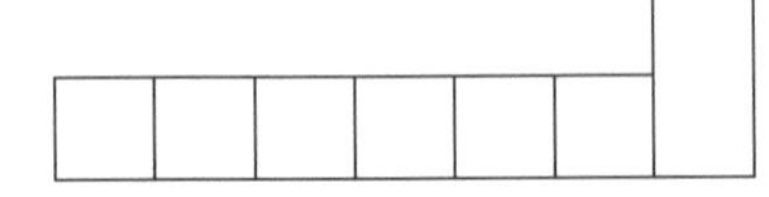

List

verb
verse
serve
environment
perform
perfect
merchant
mineral
several
concert
ambulance
modern
northern
remember
copper
customer
gardener
hunger
wander
national
member
passenger

Revision

message
cheap
tore
list
flash
leather
fail
stare
paddock
hopped
marry
eighteen
kettle
seventeen
downstairs
clothing
helicopter
library
scout
collar
crawl
fasten

9. Find these list words in the word search.

verb	remember
verse	copper
merchant	customer
perform	gardener
perfect	hunger
mineral	wander
several	serve
concert	member
modern	passenger
northern	ambulance

m	c	r	t	m	c	u	s	t	o	m	e	r
e	o	e	r	p	a	s	s	e	n	g	e	r
r	p	d	e	w	p	d	r	e	g	n	u	h
c	e	n	c	a	p	p	e	m	r	v	n	a
h	l	r	n	n	e	v	m	e	e	r	r	l
a	a	e	o	d	r	e	s	m	n	e	e	v
n	r	d	c	e	f	r	e	b	e	b	h	e
t	e	o	s	r	e	s	r	e	d	m	t	r
b	n	m	e	b	c	e	v	r	r	e	r	b
r	i	f	r	r	t	a	e	r	a	m	o	w
a	m	b	u	l	a	n	c	e	g	e	n	a
r	e	p	p	o	c	s	e	v	e	r	a	l
e	v	r	e	d	m	r	o	f	r	e	p	n

Alphabetical Order

10. Put all the list and revision words that end with 'er' into alphabetical order. (10)

Two Meanings

11. The list word 'serve' has more than one meaning. Write two sentences to show the difference.

(a)

(b)

Homonyms

12. Circle the correct word.

(a) I (wonder/wander) why she always seems to (wonder/wander) into the next classroom.

(b) All we could do was (stair, stare) as the elephant herd walked right near us.

UNIT 11

List Words	Test 1	Test 2	Test 3	Test 4	Test 5	T
(to) practise						
governor						
government						
understood						
crew						
screw						
nephew						
view						
bathe						
electronic						
electricity						
fool						
stoop						
goose						
hoof						
currant						
current						
coconut						
although						
altogether						
shoulder						
connect						

Look Say Cover Write Check

Difficult Words I Have Found	Test 1	Test 2	Test 3	T

Shape Sorter

1. Match each shape with a list word.

(a)

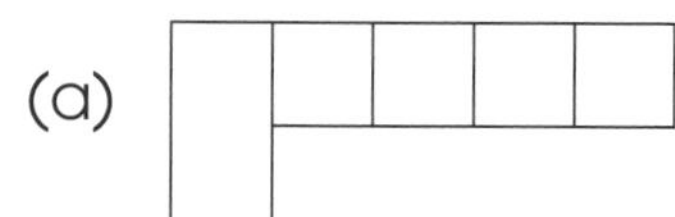

(b)

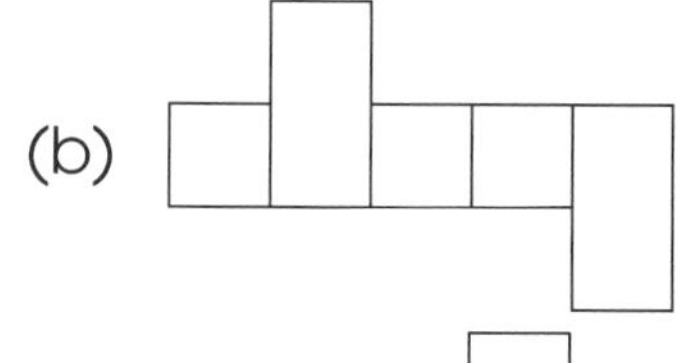

(c)

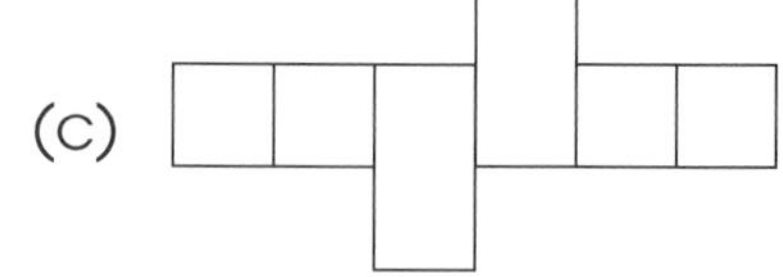

(d)

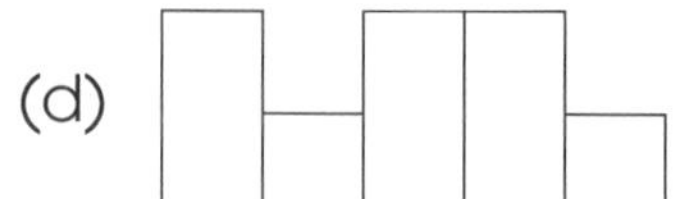

Adding Endings

2. Add suffixes to the list word 'view' to make four new words. Use a dictionary to check your answers.

____

____

____

____

3. Use list words to solve the crossword.

across

3. A horse's foot
4. To do with electrons
7. The people who rule a country
10. Trick
11. She had to __________ netball every night
13. To wash gently
14. A relative
15. The people who sail a ship
16. Happening at the present time
17. __________ it was sunny, we could not go swimming because it was too cold
18. To join
19. Wholly; completely

down

1. The flow of electric current
2. A large bird
5. Past tense of 'understand'
6. To bend down
7. The Queen's representative
8. To see
9. Used to join wood
12. Where your arm joins your body
15. A dried grape
16. A large tropical nut

Homonyms

4. Circle the correct word.

(a) Our dentist has a (practice, practise) close to my school.

(b) To play the piano well you must (practice, practise) daily.

(c) My brother's favourite cake is a sponge with cream and (currents, currants).

(d) The (current, currant) was so strong that we found it extremely difficult to swim back to shore.

Spelling Challenges

1. Write the list words using look, say, cover, write, check.
2. Jumble each revision word and give to a friend to unjumble.
3. Write the revision list in alphabetical order.
4. Use a dictionary to write a definition for each list word.

All Mixed Up

5. Unjumble the list words.

(a) foho ______ (b) rogenovr ______

(c) wevi ______ (d) phenew ______

(e) stapicer ______ (f) potos ______

(g) rantucr ______ (h) sundertodo ______

(i) conutoc ______ (j) tencurr ______

(k) theba ______ (l) lofo ______

Antonyms

6. Find a list or revision word with an opposite meaning.

(a) niece ______ (b) disconnect ______

(c) freeze ______ (d) misunderstood ______

Synonyms

7. Find a list or revision word with a similar meaning.

(a) join ______

(b) swim ______

(c) rehearse ______

(d) trick ______

(e) sight ______

(f) raisin ______

My Meanings

8. Write a definition for each of these words. Use a dictionary to check your answers.

(a) practise ______

(b) governor ______

(c) government ______

List

(to) practise
governor
government
understood
crew
screw
nephew
view
bathe
electronic
electricity
fool
stoop
goose
hoof
currant
current
coconut
although
altogether
shoulder
connect

Revision

village
peach
score
melt
frost
health
faint
square
gallop
fancy
company
eighty
settle
seventy
plaster
worth
desert
ewe
amount
microwave
lying
idea

9. **Find these list words in the word search.**

practise	governor
stoop	view
goose	government
fool	understood
crew	currant
screw	current
coconut	connect
although	nephew
hoof	altogether
bathe	shoulder

t	u	g	o	o	s	e	a	l	t	c	n	w
n	r	e	d	l	u	o	h	s	w	r	e	g
a	l	t	o	g	e	t	h	e	r	o	p	o
r	h	t	r	e	o	l	r	d	o	n	e	v
r	e	a	b	o	u	c	l	b	a	r	h	e
u	n	d	e	r	s	t	o	o	d	e	o	r
c	e	c	s	t	p	o	o	t	s	v	o	n
i	p	u	i	h	s	t	f	e	n	o	f	m
e	h	r	t	a	l	t	h	o	u	g	h	e
h	e	r	c	o	c	o	n	u	t	r	c	n
t	w	e	a	r	o	c	o	n	n	e	c	t
a	r	n	r	s	e	g	n	i	h	t	a	b
b	n	t	p	t	o	w	e	i	v	u	r	r

Missing Words

10. **Use list words to complete the sentences.**

(a) The captain spoke very clearly to his ______________ to make sure that they ______________ his instructions.

(b) The class can ______________ singing the national anthem today.

(c) ______________ it was raining, I still went walking with my ______________.

(d) To ease the pain from her aching ______________, she decided to ______________ in warm water.

(e) On the island, they drank ______________ milk and had a pet ______________.

Alphabetical Order

11. **Put the list and revision words that contain double letters in alphabetical order. For example, understood. (11)**

____

____

____

____

List Words	Test 1	Test 2	Test 3	Test 4	Test 5	T
tube						
huge						
future						
puncture						
measure						
furniture						
failure						
amuse						
refuse						
poison						
disappoint						
value						
rescue						
continue						
argue						
avenue						
reduce						
produce						
entrance						
court						
course						
virus						

Look

Say

Cover

Write

Check

Difficult Words I Have Found	Test 1	Test 2	Test 3	T

Word Worm

1. (a) Circle each list word you can find in the word worm.

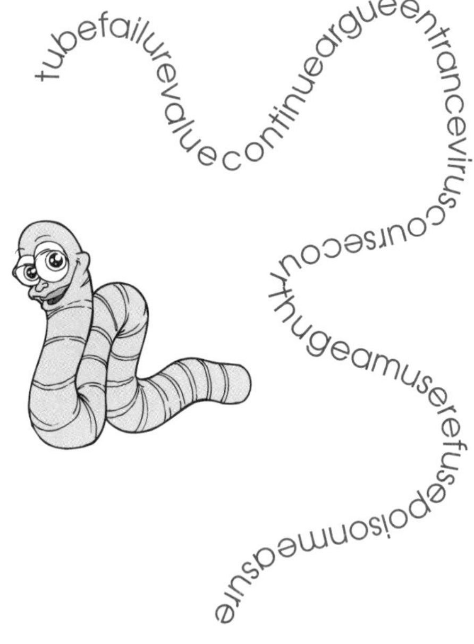

(b) Write the eight list words that are not in the word worm.

____

____

____

____

____

____

____

____

Adding Beginnings

2. The list word 'disappoint' has the prefix 'dis'. Think of three more words with the prefix 'dis'.

____

____

____

3. Use list words to solve the crossword.

across

4. To keep happy
5. A place where tennis is played
6. Worth
7. To go on
10. A type of street
11. Opposite of past
13. To make
16. Cylinder
18. A direction to follow
19. To find out the size or amount
21. A disease
22. A dangerous or harmful substance

down

1. Lack of success
2. To save from danger
3. To disagree
8. Very large
9. To put a hole in something
12. Found in a house
14. Opposite of enlarge
15. Opposite of exit
17. To let someone down
20. Deny

Missing Letters

4. Complete these list words.

(a) fu ___ ___ r ___ ________________

(b) c ___ ___rt ________________

(c) ___unc___ ___ ___e ________________

(d) ___oi___on ________________

(e) f___ ___l___ ___e ________________

(f) m___ ___su___ ___ ________________

(g) re___ ___u___ ________________

(h) am___ ___e ________________

(i) d___sa___ ___oin___ ________________

Spelling Challenges

1. Write the list words using look, say, cover, write, check.
2. Write true or false statements using the list words.
3. Sort the revision words according to the number of consonants.
4. Make word sums for the list words. For example, res + cue = rescue

Word Meanings

5. Write the list word that matches each meaning.

(a) something that can cause illness or death if swallowed __________

(b) to save someone from danger __________

(c) to disagree or quarrel __________

(d) to make something smaller __________

(e) a small organism that can cause disease __________

Antonyms

6. Find a list or revision word with an opposite meaning.

(a) uncertain __________ (b) success __________

(c) tiny __________ (d) satisfy __________

(e) exit __________ (f) unwelcome __________

Synonyms

7. Find a list or revision word with a similar meaning.

(a) enormous __________ (b) pierce __________

(c) cautious __________ (d) quarrel __________

(e) entertain __________ (f) nasty __________

Homonyms

8. Circle the correct word.

(a) The tennis tournament was played on a grass (court, caught).

(b) The batsman was (court, caught) out by the wicket-keeper.

(c) 'Of (course, coarse) I'll help you with your homework,' said my father.

(d) Hessian is a very (course, coarse) material that is usually made into sacks.

(e) We had chicken and vegetables as the main (course, coarse).

(f) The ship went off (course, coarse) because of the terrible weather.

List

tube
huge
future
puncture
measure
furniture
failure
amuse
refuse
poison
disappoint
value
rescue
continue
argue
avenue
reduce
produce
entrance
court
course
virus

Revision

voyage
least
choke
stuff
worn
tool
certain
prison
hammer
hiding
careful
welcome
whistle
glove
key
millilitre
notice
promise
drill
beginning
swam
cruel

9. Find these list words in the word search.

tube	continue
huge	argue
future	reduce
puncture	produce
measure	poison
furniture	disappoint
failure	entrance
refuse	court
value	course
rescue	virus

a	p	d	i	s	a	p	p	o	i	n	t	d
e	u	n	i	t	t	e	e	v	a	l	u	e
n	n	u	n	c	c	t	r	u	o	c	b	o
t	c	e	p	u	p	u	u	u	f	v	e	r
r	t	r	d	e	o	r	t	t	l	c	c	p
a	u	e	u	c	i	e	i	v	o	s	r	e
n	r	e	f	u	s	e	n	u	e	e	e	u
c	e	t	a	d	o	p	r	r	c	e	u	c
e	n	i	i	o	n	s	u	i	c	f	g	s
h	r	u	l	r	e	o	f	u	t	u	r	e
r	u	f	u	p	v	i	r	u	s	a	a	r
g	u	g	r	c	o	n	t	i	n	u	e	f
u	e	h	e	r	u	s	a	e	m	p	p	o

Memory Master

10. Cover the list words. Write three from memory.

______________ ______________ ______________

Write a question that contains all three words.

____

____

____

Adding Endings

11. Complete this table of suffixes.

	word	add 's'	add 'd' or 'ed'	add 'ing'
(a)	amuse	**amuses**	**amused**	**amusing**
(b)	argue			
(c)	reduce			
(d)	produce			
(e)	puncture			
(f)	poison			
(g)	rescue			
(h)	disappoint			

UNIT 13

List Words	Test 1	Test 2	Test 3	Test 4	Test 5	T
aboard						
cupboard						
flight						
virtual						
lightning						
prove						
remove						
sincere						
global						
millennium						
channel						
frozen						
extra						
cocoa						
area						
quality						
relative						
period						
obey						
musical						
judge						
cough						

Look

Say

Cover

Write

Check

Difficult Words I Have Found	Test 1	Test 2	Test 3	T

Small Words

1. Write a list word that contains these small words.

(a) light ____________

(b) rove ____________

(c) since ____________

(d) mill ____________

(e) music ____________

(f) cup ____________

(g) board ____________

(h) are ____________

Word Hunt

2. Which list words:

(a) contain 'gh'? ____________ ____________ ____________

(b) rhyme with fudge? ____________

(c) have only one vowel? ____________

3. Use list words to solve the crossword.

across

1. A duration of time
5. The clothes were of good ________
7. Surplus
13. Confirm
14. An electrical flash in the sky
16. You can climb ________ the ship now
18. A story told with music
20. The space something takes
21. Often associated with a cold

down

2. A relation
3. 1 000 years
4. Opposite of disobey
6. Frigid
8. Something that seems as if it is real
9. A storage unit
10. Honest; free from deceit
11. The power of flying
12. A passage for ships or boats
15. Globe shaped
17. To take away
19. To decide the placing in a competition
21. A drink made from seeds

Adding Beginnings

4. Match these prefixes with the list or revision words.

(a) in • • common ________

(b) un • • obey ________

(c) dis • • fortune ________

(d) un • • sincere ________

(e) mis • • frozen ________

Spelling Challenges

1. Write the list words using look, say, cover, write, check.
2. Sort the list words according to the number of vowels.
3. Write a meaningful sentence containing each of the revision words.
4. Write a paragraph containing eight list words.

UNIT 13

All Mixed Up

5. Unjumble the list words.

(a) vorpe ______ (b) rexta ______
(c) dobara ______ (d) itqyula ______
(e) lechann ______ (f) oraducbp ______
(g) giflht ______ (h) zofren ______
(i) cacoo ______ (j) yobe ______
(k) cesirne ______ (l) dejug ______

Antonyms

6. Find a list or revision word with an opposite meaning.

(a) disobey ______ (b) melted ______
(c) dishonest ______ (d) rare ______

Synonyms

7. Find a list or revision word with a similar meaning.

(a) withdraw ______ (b) kin ______
(c) enthusiastic ______ (d) solve ______

Alphabetical Order

8. Put the list and revision words that have one syllable in alphabetical order. (14)

______

______

______

______

Homonyms

9. Circle the correct word.

(a) We can go to the beach on the weekend because the (weather, whether) is going to be fine.

(b) I must decide (weather, whether) to play netball or hockey this year.

List

aboard
cupboard
flight
virtual
lightning
prove
remove
sincere
global
millennium
channel
frozen
extra
cocoa
area
quality
relative
period
obey
musical
judge
cough

Revision

bale
eager
spoke
stiff
fortune
bloom
raise
bacon
common
shining
useful
witch
stir
discover
valley
hectare
police
whether
server
rule
taught
pear

10. Find these list words in the word search.

aboard	frozen
cupboard	extra
flight	cocoa
lightning	area
prove	quality
remove	relative
sincere	period
global	obey
virtual	judge
channel	cough

c	h	g	u	o	c	l	a	u	t	r	i	v
o	s	i	g	p	e	r	i	o	d	o	r	o
g	n	i	h	t	r	e	r	e	c	n	i	s
g	c	n	n	a	b	o	a	r	d	z	c	j
n	u	c	e	c	r	o	v	l	y	e	u	o
i	p	n	i	s	e	e	b	e	o	d	y	t
n	b	n	e	z	o	r	f	e	g	n	t	h
t	o	c	o	c	o	a	e	e	y	e	i	g
h	a	c	h	a	n	n	e	l	x	t	l	i
g	r	e	m	o	v	e	q	a	y	r	a	l
i	d	u	q	p	u	c	u	e	l	x	u	f
l	e	v	i	t	a	l	e	r	e	l	q	q
o	l	a	b	o	l	g	o	a	r	t	x	e

Extend Yourself

11. (a) Write a definition for each of these words.

(i) millennium ______________________________

(ii) century ______________________________

(iii) decade ______________________________

(b) What do these words have in common? ______________________________

____

(c) Write each of the above words in a meaningful sentence.

(i) ______________________________

____

(ii) ______________________________

____

(iii) ______________________________

____

Word Meanings

12. Write the list word that matches each meaning.

(a) crushed seeds used to make chocolate ______________

(b) someone who is part of your family ______________

(c) air from your lungs when you are ill or have a tickle in your throat ______________

UNIT 14

List Words	Test 1	Test 2	Test 3	Test 4	Test 5	T
circle						
rifle						
stable						
valuable						
comfortable						
bundle						
ankle						
wrestle						
gentle						
single						
saddle						
example						
squash						
shower						
wonderful						
canoe						
cement						
caravan						
chalk						
union						
region						
million						

Look Say Cover Write Check

Difficult Words I Have Found	Test 1	Test 2	Test 3	T

Adding Beginnings

1. Add the prefix 'un' to the words below.

   (a) comfortable ____________________

   (b) stable ____________________

   (c) forgivable ____________________

   (d) available ____________________

   How does the prefix change the meaning of the word?

   Adding the prefix 'un', ____________________

   ____

   ____

Incorrect Words

2. Write these words correctly.

   (a) restle ____________________

   (b) canoo ____________________

   (c) comfortible ____________________

   (d) sqash ____________________

   (e) ancle ____________________

   (f) millon ____________________

   (g) wunderful ____________________

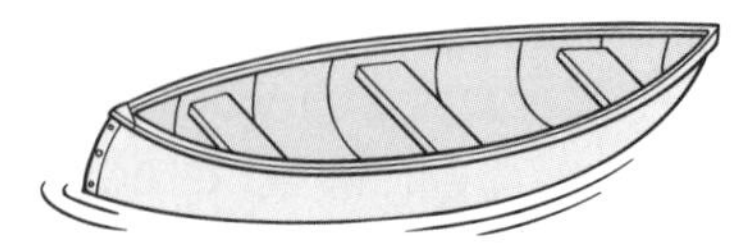

3. Use list words to solve the crossword.

across

3. A small boat powered by paddles
7. Part of the leg
9. One
10. The shape of a wheel
13. Soft or not brutal
15. A building for horses
17. A portable home
19. The new office chair was very ________
20. Strapped onto the back of a horse
21. Joining two or more things into one

down

1. Twice five hundred thousand
2. Marvellous
4. Used to stick bricks together
5. A group of things put together
6. A struggle
8. To flatten
11. A type of gun
12. Of great worth
14. A sample or model
16. A brief fall of rain
17. Used to write with on a blackboard
18. Area or district

Word Worm

4. Cross out every second letter. The leftover letters will make two revision words.

srkpiyrbtomlirnsebrz

____

____

Spelling Challenges

1. Write the list words using look, say, cover, write, check.
2. Sort the list words according to the number of syllables.
3. Make word shapes for the revision list words.
4. Use a dictionary to write definitions for five list and five revision words.

My Meanings

5. Write a definition for each of these words.
Use a dictionary to check your answers.

(a) valuable ______________________

(b) example ______________________

(c) stable ______________________

(d) wonderful ______________________

(e) region ______________________

Antonyms

6. Find a list or revision word with an opposite meaning.

(a) uncomfortable ________ (b) double ________

(c) unstable ________ (d) lumpy ________

(e) son ________ (f) western ________

Synonyms

7. Find a list or revision word with a similar meaning.

(a) precious ________ (b) gun ________

(c) area ________ (d) nothing ________

(e) tussle ________ (f) solo ________

Alphabetical Order

8. Put the list words that end in 'le' in alphabetical order. (12)

____

____

____

____

List

circle
rifle
stable
valuable
comfortable
bundle
ankle
wrestle
gentle
single
saddle
example
squash
shower
wonderful
canoe
cement
caravan
chalk
union
region
million

Revision

whale
eastern
globe
sniff
forgotten
smooth
railway
apron
suppose
miner
ought
ditch
skirt
oven
woollen
Christmas
zero
journey
shelf
microchip
daughter
vase

9. Find these list words in the word search.

circle	squash
rifle	shower
stable	wonderful
valuable	canoe
bundle	cement
ankle	caravan
wrestle	chalk
gentle	union
single	region
example	million

t	s	i	n	g	l	e	n	o	i	g	e	r
l	t	s	g	e	n	t	l	e	o	n	a	c
e	a	q	u	e	r	w	g	n	b	a	i	r
g	b	u	n	d	l	e	o	e	l	r	s	e
v	l	a	p	l	n	i	n	d	c	t	l	w
n	e	s	e	t	n	e	o	l	e	k	o	h
a	e	h	l	u	f	r	e	d	n	o	w	w
v	l	e	k	e	l	b	u	a	u	l	a	v
a	t	c	n	l	n	o	i	l	l	i	m	s
r	s	a	a	t	n	e	m	e	c	s	x	e
a	e	x	a	m	p	l	e	h	q	u	a	m
c	r	i	f	l	e	a	r	e	w	o	h	s
x	w	v	a	l	k	k	l	a	h	c	a	n

Making Adverbs

10. Add 'ly' to these list and revision words to make adverbs. Write the new word. Use a dictionary to check the spelling.

word	adverb 'ly'
comfortable	
gentle	
smooth	

Missing Words

11. Use list words to complete the sentences.

(a) The ________________ helped me to understand how to add fractions.

(b) We are only allowed to ________________ with teacher supervision, and we must be ________________ with each other.

(c) After the ________________ of hailstones, a ________________ yellow flower remained standing in the garden.

(d) The horse ran free because the ________________ was left open.

Small Words

12. Find small words in these list or revision words.

(a) comfortable ________________

(b) caravan ________________

(c) shower ________________

List Words	Test 1	Test 2	Test 3	Test 4	Test 5	T
material						
special						
harbour						
neighbour						
honour						
favour						
margarine						
juice						
ruin						
umbrella						
collect						
scene						
laptop						
scent						
anxious						
accident						
bicycle						
biscuit						
senior						
junior						
annoy						
faithfully						

Look

Say

Cover

Write

Check

Difficult Words I Have Found	Test 1	Test 2	Test 3	T

Word Challenge

1. Make as many words as you can from the word in the box. You can rearrange the letters.

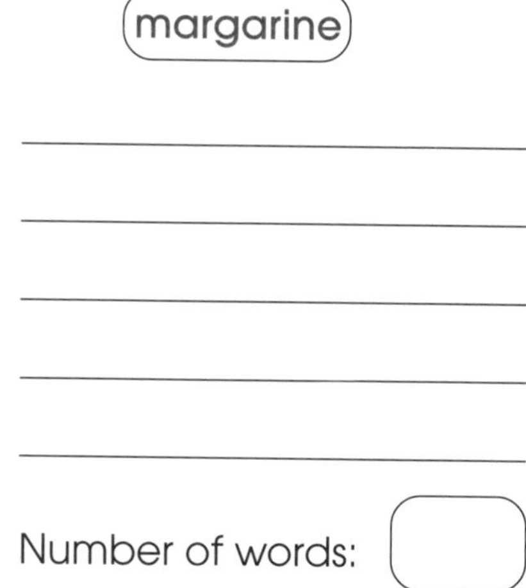

Number of words:

Shape Sorter

2. Match each shape with a list word.

(a) 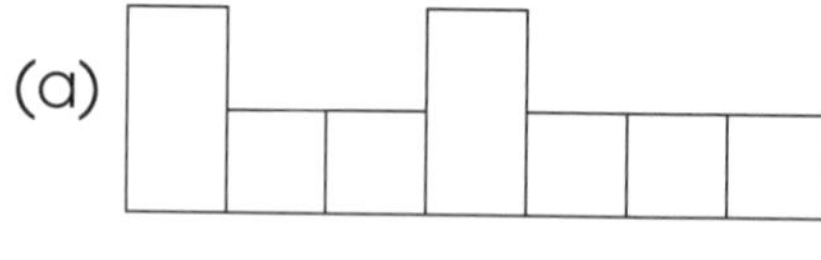

(b) 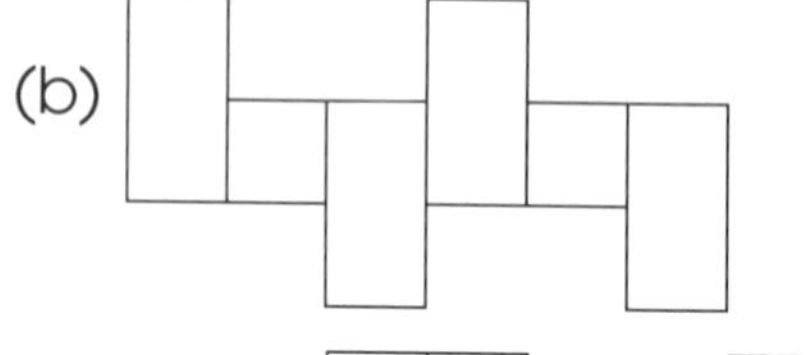

(c) 

(d) 

(e) 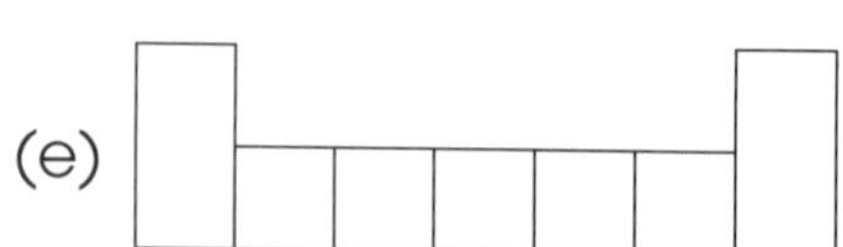

(f) 

3. Use list words to solve the crossword.

across

1. Made from fruit
2. She finished the letter 'Yours ____________'
3. Aggravate
6. A view
8. A person who lives next door
10. Prefer
14. A textile fabric
15. Nervous
17. A portable computer
18. Smell
19. A spread used on bread
20. Old in age

down

1. Young in age
4. Gather
5. A sheltered place for boats and ships
6. Exceptional
7. Recognition given for achievements
9. A 'cookie'
11. Wreck
12. Anything that happens by chance
13. Helps to keep the rain off
16. A form of transport that uses two wheels

Spelling Challenges

1. Write the list words using look, say, cover, write, check.
2. Write five silly sentences. You must use all the revision words within the sentences.
3. Write the list words in reverse alphabetical order.
4. Jumble each revision word. Give to a friend to unjumble.

All Mixed Up

4. Unjumble the list words.

(a) cindacet ______________ (b) loceltc ______________

(c) cijue ______________ (d) lemaitra ______________

(e) cesen ______________ (f) nisore ______________

(g) citibus ______________ (h) icalpse ______________

(i) brahour ______________ (j) beyiclc ______________

(k) norohu ______________ (l) gonebiurh ______________

Antonyms

5. Find a list or revision word with an opposite meaning.

(a) dishonour ______________ (b) wild ______________

(c) bent ______________ (d) incorrect ______________

Synonyms

6. Find a list or revision word with a similar meaning.

(a) clever ______________ (b) port ______________

(c) parasol ______________ (d) uneasy ______________

(e) scruffy ______________ (f) spoil ______________

Homonyms

7 Circle the correct words.

(a) The (seen, scene) from the aircraft window was quite spectacular.

(b) Many people claim to have (seen, scene) UFOs.

(c) The (sent, scent, cent) of the flowers filled the room.

(d) I (sent, scent, cent) my grandfather a card for his birthday.

(e) A coin worth a hundredth of a dollar is called a (sent, scent, cent).

Alphabetical Order

8. Put the list and revision words that contain double letters in alphabetical order. For example, collect. (9)

____

____

____

List

material
special
harbour
neighbour
honour
favour
margarine
juice
ruin
umbrella
collect
scene
laptop
scent
anxious
accident
bicycle
biscuit
senior
junior
annoy
faithfully

Revision

tame
cinema
dose
patch
history
choose
smart
stock
correct
spider
fought
match
thirsty
dozen
tonne
beauty
piano
signal
reason
camel
straight
ragged

9. Find these list words in the word search.

special	scent
harbour	anxious
neighbour	accident
honour	bicycle
margarine	biscuit
juice	senior
ruin	junior
umbrella	annoy
scene	faithfully
laptop	collect

n	e	r	y	l	l	u	f	h	t	i	a	f
i	o	o	h	r	h	a	r	b	o	u	r	y
b	m	i	s	u	o	i	x	n	a	b	t	o
a	a	n	c	o	t	a	n	n	o	y	i	b
c	r	u	m	b	r	e	l	l	a	r	u	r
c	g	j	i	h	l	a	p	t	o	p	c	a
i	a	a	r	g	i	d	r	u	o	n	o	h
d	r	u	b	i	c	y	c	l	e	e	v	o
e	i	s	c	e	n	t	j	u	n	c	s	e
n	n	s	e	n	i	o	r	c	c	s	c	l
t	e	s	t	c	e	l	l	o	c	i	e	l
j	l	t	i	u	c	s	i	b	u	i	n	u
u	s	p	e	c	i	a	l	j	l	y	e	v

Memory Master

10. Cover the list words. Write three from memory.

__________ __________ __________

Write an interesting sentence using all three words.

____

____

____

Adding Endings

11. Add as many of these suffixes as possible to the list and revision words given.

(a) honour ____________________

(b) bicycle ____________________

(c) annoy ____________________

(d) material ____________________

(e) neighbour ____________________

(f) special ____________________

(g) correct ____________________

UNIT 16

List Words	Test 1	Test 2	Test 3	Test 4	Test 5	T
niece						
handkerchief						
centre						
CD Rom						
tongue						
truly						
pilot						
bough						
graphic						
document						
garage						
halves						
cardigan						
careless						
knot						
lettuce						
bother						
palm						
equal						
type						
byte						
repair						

Look

Say

Cover

Write

Check

Difficult Words I Have Found	Test 1	Test 2	Test 3	T

Small Words

1. Write a list word which contains these small words.

(a) hand ______________

(b) card ______________

(c) pair ______________

(d) rage ______________

(e) care ______________

(f) her ______________

(g) graph ______________

ɿoɿɿiM Writing

2. Complete the mirror writing.

(a) moЯ DƆ |

(b) | halves

(c) ɘugnot |

(d) | bough

(e) | knot

(f) lɒupɘ |

(g) ɘqyt |

(h) | careless

(i) | lettuce

3. Use list words to solve the crossword.

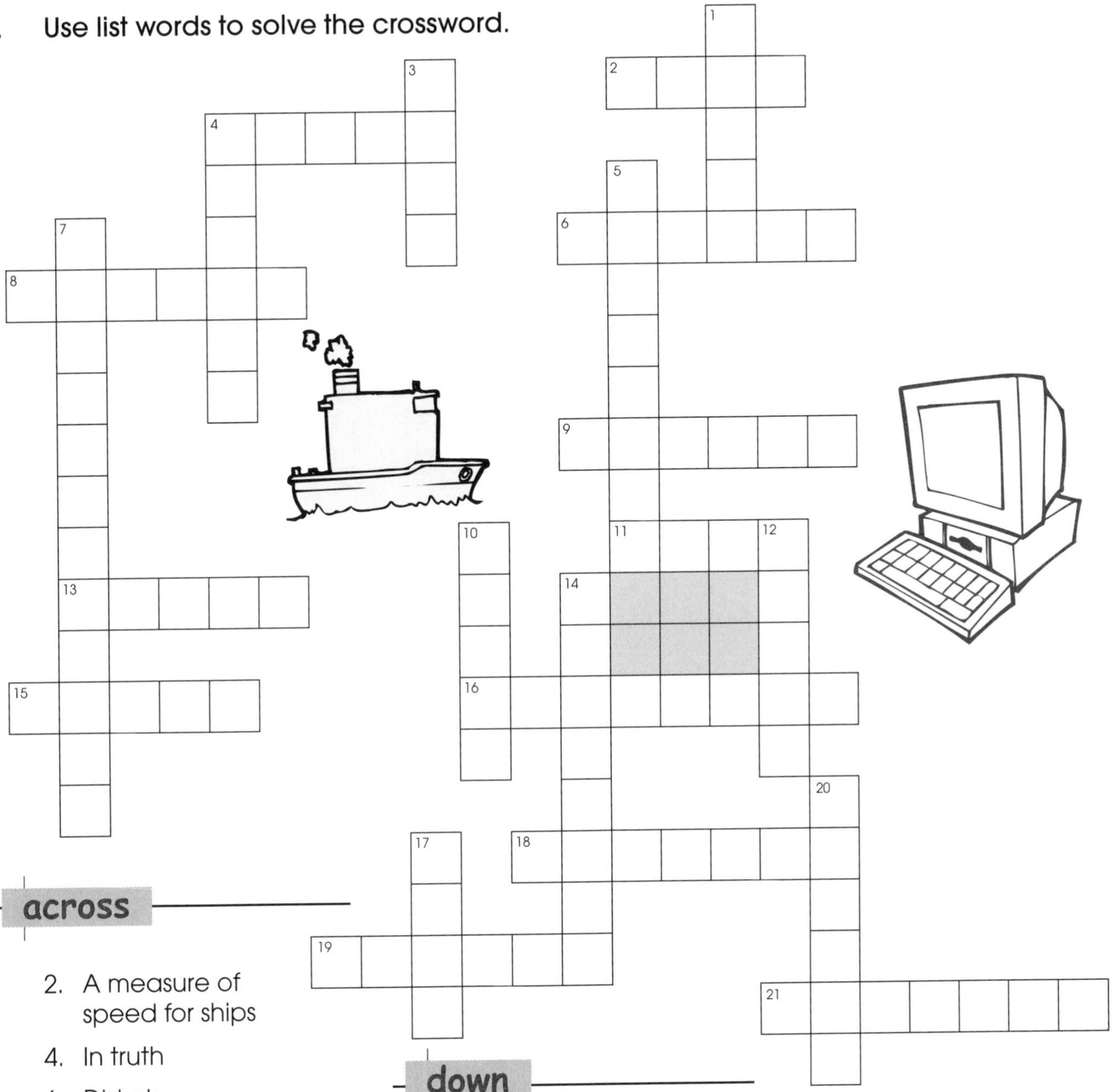

across

2. A measure of speed for ships
4. In truth
6. Disturb
8. A building for storing cars
9. Fix
11. Kind
13. A compact disc that holds writing, sound and pictures for a computer
15. The person who flies an aeroplane
16. A type of knitted jacket
18. A green salad vegetable
19. Two equal parts of a whole.
21. A diagram or graph

down

1. A branch of a tree
3. A unit of information stored on computer
4. Found in the mouth
5. A paper with information
7. A cloth used to wipe the nose
10. A relative
12. Equivalent
14. Negligent
17. Part of the hand
20. The part in the middle

Spelling Challenges

1. Write the list words using look, say, cover, write, check.
2. Sort the revision words according to the number of syllables.
3. Use a dictionary to write a definition for 10 list words.
4. Write the revision list in alphabetical order.

Missing Letters

4. Complete these list and revision words.

(a) p___ ___m __________

(b) b___ ___g___ __________

(c) ___ra___ ___ic __________

(d) ___on___ue __________

(e) b___ ___e __________

Antonyms

5. Find a list or revision word with an opposite meaning.

(a) nephew __________ (b) careful __________

(c) loose __________ (d) wife __________

Synonyms

6. Find a list or revision word with a similar meaning.

(a) fix __________ (b) middle __________

(c) honestly __________ (d) lady __________

(e) faulty __________ (f) annoy __________

Homonyms

7. Circle the correct words.

(a) The (bow, bough) of the tree was tapping against the window.

(b) It is a Japanese custom to (bow, bough) when you meet someone.

(c) The (not, knot) in my shoelace was very difficult to undo.

(d) 'I will (not, knot) go to bed!' said the naughty child.

More Than One

8. Complete this table of plurals.

(a)	market	
(b)		buttons
(c)	graphic	
(d)	woman	
(e)		halves

List

niece
handkerchief
centre
CD Rom
tongue
truly
pilot
bough
graphic
document
garage
halves
cardigan
careless
knot
lettuce
bother
palm
equal
type
byte
repair

Revision

flame
recycle
vote
prey
report
tight
market
scan
button
broken
woman
butcher
autumn
soup
crept
sixty
radio
through
lemon
towel
husband
remind

9. Find these list words in the word search.

niece	halves
handkerchief	cardigan
centre	careless
tongue	knot
truly	lettuce
pilot	bother
bough	palm
graphic	equal
CD-Rom	byte
garage	repair

g	a	r	p	l	n	g	r	a	p	h	i	c
e	g	a	p	m	s	s	e	l	e	r	a	c
n	l	e	t	t	u	c	e	d	h	s	t	e
m	g	a	r	a	g	e	t	b	a	o	k	n
e	x	g	p	i	s	h	s	y	l	u	r	t
b	e	l	a	u	q	e	l	i	v	s	h	r
v	o	q	t	o	n	n	p	o	e	s	a	e
t	b	u	e	l	i	d	y	t	s	e	l	t
t	o	n	g	u	e	k	C	D	R	o	m	o
h	t	n	r	h	e	a	r	d	i	g	a	n
i	h	c	k	e	e	j	g	p	a	f	d	o
f	e	i	h	c	r	e	k	d	n	a	h	u
e	r	e	p	a	i	r	k	u	e	t	y	b

Word Worm

10. (a) Circle each list word you can find in the word worm.

(b) Write the eight list words that are not in the word worm.

______ ______ ______ ______

______ ______ ______ ______

Word Hunt

11. Which list or revision words:

(a) have a silent 'l'?

______ ______

(b) rhyme with light?

______ ______

(c) have an 'er' sound?

______ ______ ______

(d) have three syllables?

______ ______ ______

______ ______ ______

List Words	Test 1	Test 2	Test 3	Test 4	Test 5	T
sauce						
communicate						
sausage						
question						
composition						
addition						
attention						
condition						
direction						
examination						
position						
population						
nation						
international						
dictionary						
guard						
guess						
guest						
guide						
southern						
double						
whom						

Look

Say

Cover

Write

Check

Difficult Words I Have Found	Test 1	Test 2	Test 3	T

Magic Words

1. Change the first word into the last by changing one letter on each line to make a new word. For example:

loan
load
road
read
reed

(a) whom

____
____
____

clip

(b) tyre

____
____
____

limp

Small Words

2. Find small words in these list words.

(a) whom

____

(b) addition

____

(c) direction

____

(d) international

____

(e) examination

____

3. Use list words to solve the crossword.

across

2. To give an answer without really knowing
5. A liquid seasoning
8. To show the way
10. A type of meat made into a tube
11. To show concentration
12. A piece of writing
14. To __________ it may concern
16. Instruction
18. Place
19. A visitor
20. A book that explains the meaning of words

down

1. To share thoughts or feelings
2. Protect
3. The number of people in a country
4. An important test
6. Opposite of subtraction
7. Opposite of answer
9. The state of something
13. Opposite of northern
15. Country
17. Twice as much

Spelling Challenges

1. Write the list words using look, say, cover, write, check.
2. Jumble the revision words. Give to a friend to unjumble.
3. Sort the list words according to your own rule. Can a friend guess the rule?
4. Write each of the list words in a question.

Homonyms

4. Circle the correct word.

   (a) It will (tyre, tire) my grandfather if he changes the (tyre, tire) on his own.

   (b) Remember to bring the tomato (source, sauce) to the picnic.

   (c) When your project is finished, write the (source, sauce) of information on the last page.

Alphabetical Order

5. Put the list words with the 'tion' sound in alphabetical order. (12)

____

____

____

____

Synonyms

6. Find a list or revision word with a similar meaning.

   (a) people ____________ (b) quiet ____________

   (c) team ____________ (d) essay ____________

   (e) protect ____________ (f) visitor ____________

My Meanings

7. Write a definition for each of these words.
   Use a dictionary to check your answers.

   (a) composition ______________________________

   ____

   (b) dictionary ______________________________

   ____

   (c) double ______________________________

   ____

   (d) guest ______________________________

   ____

   ____

List

sauce
communicate
sausage
question
composition
addition
attention
condition
direction
examination
position
population
nation
international
dictionary
guard
guess
guest
guide
southern
double
whom

Revision

taste
loan
stole
press
important
fright
march
calculator
mutton
blanket
women
newspaper
cause
group
secret
tyre
silent
couple
motor
hotel
receive
erosion

8. Find these list words in the word search.

sauce	nation
sausage	international
question	dictionary
composition	guard
addition	guess
attention	guest
condition	guide
direction	southern
position	double
population	whom

c	d	a	t	t	e	n	t	i	o	n	i	l
o	n	i	i	o	n	o	i	t	i	d	d	a
m	o	n	c	s	n	r	l	n	n	x	p	n
p	i	b	k	t	o	n	z	f	o	g	o	o
o	t	d	t	s	i	u	j	o	i	u	s	i
s	a	r	s	a	t	o	t	h	t	i	i	t
i	l	n	e	u	s	g	n	h	c	d	t	a
t	u	a	u	s	e	u	g	a	e	e	i	n
i	p	t	g	a	u	e	u	k	r	r	o	r
o	o	i	m	g	q	s	a	n	i	y	n	e
n	p	o	l	e	t	s	r	q	d	w	v	t
m	h	n	k	c	o	n	d	i	t	i	o	n
w	e	l	b	u	o	d	s	a	u	c	e	i

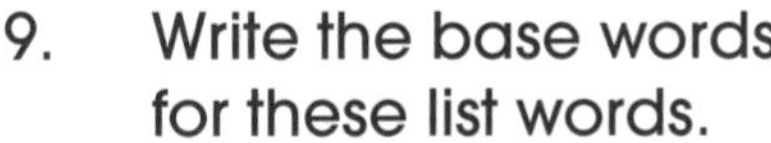

Base Words

9. Write the base words for these list words.

(a) composition compose

(b) population ____________

(c) examination ____________

(d) direction ____________

(e) southern ____________

(f) calculator ____________

In The Past

10. Complete this table of list and revision words.

present	past
	doubled
taste	
	guessed
question	
	stole
	received
march	

Adding Endings

11. Complete this table of suffixes.

	word	add 's' or 'es'	add 'd' or 'ed'	add 'ing'
(a)	question		questioned	
(b)		positions		positioning
(c)	guess		guessed	
(d)				doubling
(e)	group			
(f)			received	

List Words	Test 1	Test 2	Test 3	Test 4	Test 5	T
possible						
horrible						
article						
swarm						
wharf						
violet						
violin						
whisper						
youth						
business						
carriage						
wreck						
concrete						
console						
imagine						
marriage						
museum						
barrier						
yacht						
neither						
usual						
experience						

Look Say Cover Write Check

Difficult Words I Have Found	Test 1	Test 2	Test 3	T

Shape Sorter

1. Match each shape with a list word.

(a) 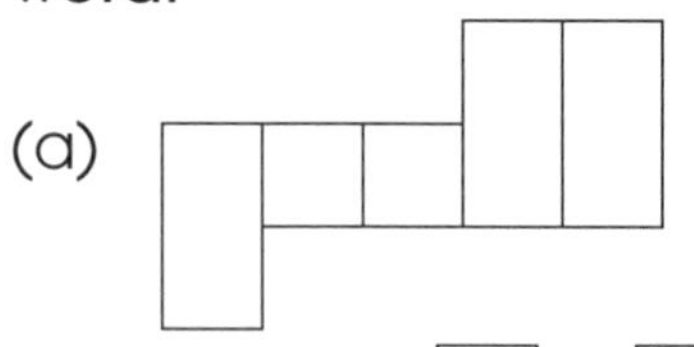

(b) 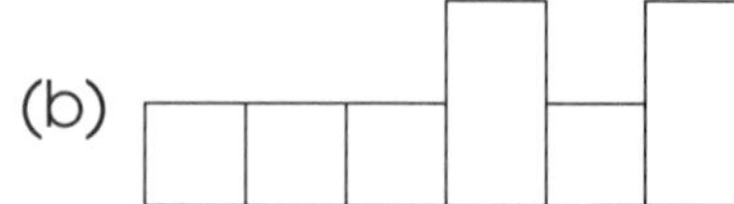

(c) 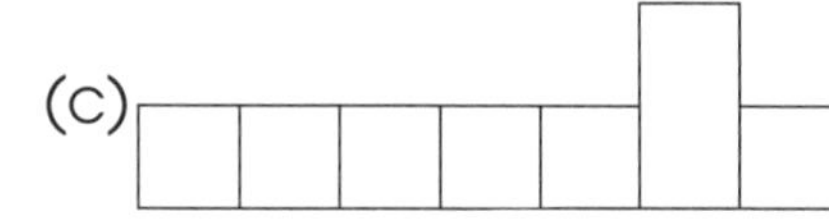

(d) 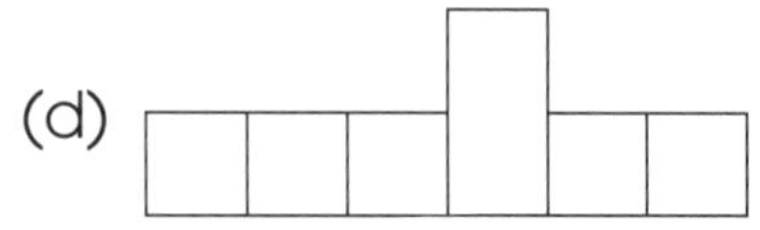

(e) 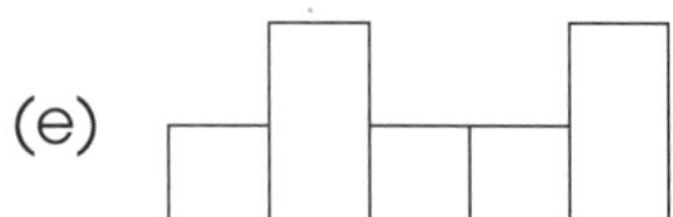

Adding Endings

2. Choose a suffix to add to these list and revision words.

'ly' 'ing' 'ful' 'ment'

(a) horrible ______________

(b) imagine ______________

(c) punish ______________

____

(d) possible ______________

(e) waste ______________

____

3. Use list words to solve the crossword.

across

1. Wedlock
3. A wind-powered boat
5. A building which exhibits objects of interest to the public
6. Protective fence
7. A mixture of broken stones and cement
9. To talk very quietly
10. Ruin
12. Being able to do
14. ________ of us is well enough to go to school
18. A thing or object
20. A control panel
21. The early part of life

down

2. To think or suppose
4. Your work or your job
7. The part of a train that carries people
8. A musical instrument
11. Terrible
13. A ________ of bees
15 A personal encounter
16. A quay
17. A type of flowering plant
19. Opposite of unusual

Spelling Challenges

1. Write the words using look, say, cover, write, check.
2. Write the revision list in reverse alphabetical order.
3. Sort the list words according to the number of vowels in each word.
4. Write a paragraph containing all of the list words.

Missing Words

4. Use list words to complete the sentences.

   (a) We were told to close our eyes and ________________ our future.

   (b) When they travel to the city, they sit in the third ________________ on the train.

   (c) ________________ of the children would admit to spilling the glue.

   (d) 'Would it be ________________ for Sarah to sleep over tonight?' asked the girl.

   (e) The cat made little paw prints as it walked across the fresh ________________.

   (f) It was ________________ for him to be late on a Thursday because he had ________________ practice.

Antonyms

5. Find a list or revision word with an opposite meaning.

   (a) impossible ________________ (b) shout ________________

   (c) foreigner ________________ (d) reward ________________

   (e) cooked ________________ (f) unusual ________________

Synonyms

6. Find a list or revision word with a similar meaning.

   (a) adolescent ________________ (b) union ________________

   (c) lilac ________________ (d) mistake ________________

My Meanings

7. Write a definition for each of these words. Use a dictionary to check your answers.

   (a) swarm ________________

   (b) violet ________________

   (c) barrier ________________

   (d) wharf ________________

List

possible
horrible
article
swarm
wharf
violet
violin
whisper
youth
business
carriage
wreck
concrete
console
imagine
marriage
museum
barrier
yacht
neither
usual
experience

Revision

waste
coast
cloud
print
error
midnight
charge
bucket
tunnel
punish
lately
raw
saucer
either
safety
telephone
sentence
unless
visitor
axe
native
greenhouse

8. Find these list words in the word search.

possible	wreck
horrible	concrete
article	console
swarm	imagine
wharf	museum
violet	barrier
violin	yacht
whisper	neither
youth	usual
business	experience

e	b	w	h	i	s	p	e	r	j	k	b	e
n	m	u	s	e	u	m	e	e	b	e	h	x
i	c	o	m	k	t	c	l	i	o	t	o	p
g	k	c	e	r	w	o	l	r	n	e	r	e
a	n	t	s	b	t	n	t	r	i	r	r	r
m	i	k	q	u	c	s	r	a	r	c	i	i
i	l	n	b	s	n	o	l	b	e	n	b	e
p	o	s	s	i	b	l	e	r	h	o	l	n
f	i	w	t	n	h	e	i	b	t	c	e	c
r	v	a	k	e	t	e	l	o	i	v	i	e
a	a	r	r	s	u	k	n	t	e	n	o	i
h	b	m	w	s	o	l	r	d	n	s	n	k
w	t	h	c	a	y	a	u	s	u	a	l	m

Memory Master

9. Cover the list words. Write three from memory.

____________ ____________ ____________

Write an interesting question using all three words.

____

____

Missing Letters

10. Complete these list and revision words.

(a) ex___ ___ ___ ___ence ____________

(b) h___ ___ ___ ___ble ____________

(c) ___s___al ____________

(d) ___ ___uth ____________

(e) ___oa___ ___ ____________

Two Meanings

11. The list word 'console' has more than one meaning. Write two sentences to show the difference.

(a) ____________________________________

____

(b) ____________________________________

____

Interesting Words from my Writing

Date	Word	Date	Word	Date	Word

Interesting Words from my Writing

Date	Word	Date	Word	Date	Word

My Dictionary Words: Aa to Ii

Aa

Bb

Cc

Dd

Ee

Ff

Gg

Hh

Ii

My Dictionary Words: Jj to Rr

Jj

Kk

Ll

Mm

Nn

Oo

Pp

Qq

Rr

My Dictionary Words: Ss to Zz